PR
4070
.E96
v.1

Barrie, Sir James Matthew, bart., 1860-1937.
    The novels, tales and sketches of J. M.
Barrie. New York, C. Scribner's sons,
1896-1911.
    12 v. fronts. (v. 1 : port.) plates.
22 cm.
On verse of t.p. : Author's edition.
    CONTENTS.--v. 1. Auld licht idylls.
Better dead.--v. 2. When a man's single.--
v. 3. A window in Thrums. An Edinburgh
eleven.--v. 4-5. The little minister.--

(continued next card)

J. M. BARRIE

Vol. I

AULD LICHT IDYLLS
BETTER DEAD ❧ ❧ ❧

From photograph by permission of Fredᵏ Hollyer

J. M. BARRIE.

THE NOVELS, TALES AND SKETCHES OF J. M. BARRIE

AULD LICHT IDYLLS BETTER DEAD

PUBLISHED IN NEW YORK BY CHARLES SCRIBNER'S SONS 1896

AUTHOR'S EDITION

J. M. Barrie

Copyright, 1896, by CHARLES SCRIBNER'S SONS.

51305

TO

FREDERICK GREENWOOD

INTRODUCTION

THIS is the only American edition of my books produced with my sanction, and I have special reasons for thanking Messrs. Scribner for its publication; they let it be seen, by this edition, what are my books, for I know not how many volumes purporting to be by me, are in circulation in America which are no books of mine. I have seen several of these, bearing such titles as "Two of Them," "An Auld Licht Manse," "A Tillyloss Scandal," and some of them announce themselves as author's editions, or published by arrangement with the author. They consist of scraps collected and published without my knowledge, and I entirely disown them. I have written no books save those that appear in this edition.

I am asked to write a few lines on the front page of each of these volumes, to say something, as I take it, about how they came into being. Well, they were written mainly to please one woman who is now dead, but as I am writing a little book about my mother I shall say no more of her here.

INTRODUCTION

Many of the chapters in "Auld Licht Idylls" first apppeared in a different form in the *St. James's Gazette*, and there is little doubt that they would never have appeared anywhere but for the encouragement given to me by the editor of that paper. It was pressure from him that induced me to write a second "Idyll" and a third after I thought the first completed the picture, he set me thinking seriously of these people, and though he knew nothing of them himself, may be said to have led me back to them. It seems odd, and yet I am not the first nor the fiftieth who has left Thrums at sunrise to seek the life-work that was all the time awaiting him at home. And we seldom sally forth a second time. I had always meant to be a novelist, but London, I thought, was the quarry.

For long I had an uneasy feeling that no one save the editor read my contributions, for I was leading a lonely life in London, and not another editor could I find in the land willing to print the Scotch dialect. The magazines, Scotch and English, would have nothing to say to me — I think I tried them all with "The Courting of T'nowhead's Bell," but it never found shelter until it got within book-covers. In time, however, I found another paper, the *British Weekly*, with an editor as bold as my first (or shall we say he suffered from the same infirmity?). He revived my drooping hopes, and I was again able to turn to the only kind of literary

work I now seemed to have much interest in. He
let me sign my articles, which was a big step for
me and led to my having requests for work from
elsewhere, but always the invitations said "not
Scotch—the public will not read dialect." By this
time I had put together from these two sources
and from my drawerful of rejected stories this
book of "Auld Licht Idylls," and in its collected
form it again went the rounds. I offered it to certain firms as a gift, but they would not have it
even at that. And then, on a day came actually
an offer for it from Messrs. Hodder and Stoughton.
For this, and for many another kindness, I had the
editor of the *British Weekly* to thank. Thus the
book was published at last, and as for Messrs.
Hodder and Stoughton I simply dare not say what
a generous firm I found them, lest it send too
many aspirants to their doors. But, indeed, I have
had the pleasantest relations with all my publishers.

"Better Dead " is, by my wish, no longer on
sale in Great Britain, and I should have preferred
not to see it here, for it is in no way worthy of
the beautiful clothes Messrs. Scribner have given
it. Weighted with "An Edinburgh Eleven" it
would rest very comfortably in the mill dam, but
the publishers have reasons for its inclusion;
among them, I suspect, is a well-grounded fear
that if I once began to hack and hew, I should

not stop until I had reduced the edition to two volumes. This juvenile effort is a field of prickles into which none may be advised to penetrate—I made the attempt lately in cold blood and came back shuddering, but I had read enough to have the profoundest reason for declining to tell what the book is about. And yet I have a sentimental interest in "Better Dead," for it was my first—published when I had small hope of getting any one to accept the Scotch—and there was a week when I loved to carry it in my pocket and did not think it dead weight. Once I almost saw it find a purchaser. She was a pretty girl and it lay on a bookstall, and she read some pages and smiled, and then retired, and came back and began another chapter. Several times she did this, and I stood in the background trembling with hope and fear. At last she went away without the book, but I am still of opinion that, had it been just a little bit better, she would have bought it.

CONTENTS

AULD LICHT IDYLLS

BETTER DEAD

AULD LICHT IDYLLS

AULD LICHT IDYLLS

CHAPTER I

THE SCHOOLHOUSE

EARLY this morning I opened a window in my schoolhouse in the glen of Quharity, awakened by the shivering of a starving sparrow against the frosted glass. As the snowy sash creaked in my hand, he made off to the water-spout that suspends its "tangles" of ice over a gaping tank, and, rebounding from that, with a quiver of his little black breast, bobbed through the network of wire and joined a few of his fellows in a forlorn hop round the henhouse in search of food. Two days ago my hilarious bantam-cock, saucy to the last, my cheeriest companion, was found frozen in his own water-trough, the corn-saucer in three pieces by his side. Since then I have taken the hens into the house. At meal-times they litter the hearth with each other's feathers; but for the most part they give little

1

trouble, roosting on the rafters of the low-roofed kitchen among staves and fishing-rods.

Another white blanket has been spread upon the glen since I looked out last night; for over the same wilderness of snow that has met my gaze for a week, I see the steading of Waster Lunny sunk deeper into the waste. The schoolhouse, I suppose, serves similarly as a snowmark for the people at the farm. Unless that is Waster Lunny's grieve foddering the cattle in the snow, not a living thing is visible. The ghostlike hills that pen in the glen have ceased to echo to the sharp crack of the sportsman's gun (so clear in the frosty air as to be a warning to every rabbit and partridge in the valley); and only giant Catlaw shows here and there a black ridge, rearing its head at the entrance to the glen and struggling ineffectually to cast off his shroud. Most wintry sign of all, I think as I close the window hastily, is the open farm-stile, its poles lying embedded in the snow where they were last flung by Waster Lunny's herd. Through the still air comes from a distance a vibration as of a tuning-fork: a robin, perhaps, alighting on the wire of a broken fence.

In the warm kitchen, where I dawdle over my breakfast, the widowed bantam-hen has perched on the back of my drowsy cat. It is needless to go through the form of opening the school to-day;

for, with the exception of Waster Lunny's girl, I have had no scholars for nine days. Yesterday she announced that there would be no more schooling till it was fresh, "as she wasna comin';" and indeed, though the smoke from the farm chimneys is a pretty prospect for a snowed-up schoolmaster, the trudge between the two houses must be weary work for a bairn. As for the other children, who have to come from all parts of the hills and glen, I may not see them for weeks. Last year the school was practically deserted for a month. A pleasant outlook, with the March examinations staring me in the face, and an inspector fresh from Oxford. I wonder what he would say if he saw me to-day digging myself out of the schoolhouse with the spade I now keep for the purpose in my bedroom.

The kail grows brittle from the snow in my dank and cheerless garden. A crust of bread gathers timid pheasants round me. The robins, I see, have made the coalhouse their home. Waster Lunny's dog never barks without rousing my sluggish cat to a joyful response. It is Dutch courage with the birds and beasts of the glen, hard driven for food; but I look attentively for them in these long forenoons, and they have begun to regard me as one of themselves. My breath freezes, despite my pipe, as I peer from the door; and with a fortnight-old newspaper I retire

3

to the ingle-nook. The friendliest thing I have seen to-day is the well-smoked ham suspended from my kitchen rafters. It was a gift from the farm of Tullin, with a load of peats, the day before the snow began to fall. I doubt if I have seen a cart since.

This afternoon I was the not altogether passive spectator of a curious scene in natural history. My feet encased in stout "tackety" boots, I had waded down two of Waster Lunny's fields to the glen burn: in summer the never-failing larder from which, with wriggling worm or garish fly, I can any morning whip a savoury breakfast; in the winter-time the only thing in the valley that defies the ice-king's chloroform. I watched the water twisting black and solemn through the snow, the ragged ice on its edge proof of the toughness of the struggle with the frost, from which it has, after all, crept only half victorious. A bare wild rose-bush on the further bank was violently agitated, and then there ran from its root a black-headed rat with wings. Such was the general effect. I was not less interested when my startled eyes divided this phenomenon into its component parts, and recognized in the disturbance on the opposite bank only another fierce struggle among the hungry animals for existence: they need no professor to teach them the doctrine of the survival of the fittest. A weasel had gripped a water-hen (whit-rit and beltie they are called in these parts) cowering at the root of the rose-bush, and was being dragged down the bank by the terrified bird, which made for the water as its only chance of escape. In less disadvantageous circumstances the weasel would have made short work of his victim; but as he only had the bird by the tail, the prospects of the combatants were equalized. It was the tug-of-war being played with a life as the stakes. "If I do not reach the water," was the argument that went on in the heaving little breast of the one, "I am a dead bird." "If this water-hen," reasoned the other, "reaches the burn, my supper vanishes with her." Down the sloping bank the hen had distinctly the best of it, but after that came a yard of level snow, and here she tugged and screamed in vain. I had so far been an unobserved spectator; but my sympathies were with the beltie, and, thinking it high time to interfere, I jumped into the water. The water-hen gave one mighty final tug and toppled into the burn; while the weasel viciously showed me his teeth, and then stole slowly up the bank to the rose-bush, whence, "girning," he watched me lift his exhausted victim from the water, and set off with her for the schoolhouse. Except for her draggled tail, she already looks wonderfully composed, and so long as the frost holds I shall have little difficulty in keeping her with me. On Sunday I found a frozen sparrow,

5

whose heart had almost ceased to beat, in the disused pig-sty, and put him for warmth into my breast-pocket. The ungrateful little scrub bolted without a word of thanks about ten minutes afterwards to the alarm of my cat, which had not known his whereabouts.

I am alone in the schoolhouse. On just such an evening as this last year my desolation drove me to Waster Lunny, where I was storm-stayed for the night. The recollection decides me to court my own warm hearth, to challenge my right hand again to a game at the " dambrod " against my left. I do not lock the schoolhouse door at nights; for even a highwayman (there is no such luck) would be received with open arms, and I doubt if there be a barred door in all the glen. But it is cosier to put on the shutters. The road to Thrums has lost itself miles down the valley. I wonder what they are doing out in the world. Though I am the Free Church precentor in Thrums (ten pounds a year, and the little town is five miles away), they have not seen me for three weeks. A packman whom I thawed yesterday at my kitchen fire tells me, that last Sabbath only the Auld Lichts held service. Other people realized that they were snowed up. Far up the glen, after it twists out of view, a manse and half a dozen thatched cottages that are there may still show a candle light, and the crumbling gravestones keep cold vigil round the grey old kirk.   Heavy shadows fade into the sky to the north.   A flake trembles against the window; but it is too cold for much snow to-night.   The shutter bars the outer world from the schoolhouse.

CHAPTER II

Thrums is the name I give here to the handful of
houses jumbled together in a cup, which is the
town nearest the schoolhouse. Until twenty years
ago its every other room, earthen-floored and showing the rafters overhead, had a handloom, and hun-
dreds of weavers lived and died Thoreaus " ben the
hoose " without knowing it. In those days the
cup overflowed and left several houses on the top
of the hill, where their cold skeletons still stand.
The road that climbs from the square, which is
Thrums's heart, to the north is so steep and straight,
that in a sharp frost children hunker at the top and
are blown down with a roar and a rush on rails of
ice. At such times, when viewed from the cemetery where the traveller from the schoolhouse gets
his first glimpse of the little town, Thrums is but
two church steeples and a dozen red stone patches
standing out of a snow-heap. One of the steeples
belongs to the new Free Kirk, and the other to the
parish church, both of which the first Auld Licht
minister I knew ran past when he had not time to

8

avoid them by taking a back wynd. He was but a pocket edition of a man, who grew two inches after he was called; but he was so full of the cure of souls, that he usually scudded to it with his coat-tails quarrelling behind him. His successor, whom I knew better, was a greater scholar, and said, "Let us see what this is in the original Greek," as an ordinary man might invite a friend to dinner; but he never wrestled as Mr. Dishart, his successor, did with the pulpit cushions, nor flung himself at the pulpit door. Nor was he so "hard on the Book," as Lang Tammas, the precentor, expressed it, meaning that he did not bang the Bible with his fist as much as might have been wished.

Thrums had been known to me for years before I succeeded the captious dominie at the school-house in the glen. The dear old soul who origi-nally induced me to enter the Auld Licht kirk by lamenting the "want of Christ" in the minister's discourses was my first landlady. For the last ten years of her life she was bedridden, and only her interest in the kirk kept her alive. Her case against the minister was that he did not call to denounce her sufficiently often for her sins, her pleasure being to hear him bewailing her on his knees as one who was probably past praying for. She was as sweet and pure a woman as I ever knew, and had her wishes been horses, she would have sold them and kept (and looked after) a minister herself.

AULD LICHT IDYLLS

There are few Auld Licht communities in Scotland nowadays — perhaps because people are now so well off, for the most devout Auld Lichts were always poor, and their last years were generally a grim struggle with the workhouse. Many a heavy-eyed, back-bent weaver has won his Waterloo in Thrums fighting on his stumps. There are a score or two of them left still, for, though there are now two factories in the town, the clatter of the hand-loom can yet be heard, and they have been starving themselves of late until they have saved up enough money to get another minister.

The square is packed away in the centre of Thrums, and irregularly built little houses squeeze close to it like chickens clustering round a hen. Once the Auld Lichts held property in the square, but other denominations have bought them out of it, and now few of them are even to be found in the main streets that make for the rim of the cup. They live in the kirk-wynd, or in retiring little houses the builder of which does not seem to have remembered that it is a good plan to have a road leading to houses until after they were finished. Narrow paths straggling round gardens, some of them with stunted gates, which it is commoner to step over than to open, have been formed to reach these dwellings, but in winter they are running streams, and then the best way to reach a house such as that of Tammy Mealmaker the wright, pronounced wir-icht, is over a broken dyke and a pig-sty. Tammy, who died a bachelor, had been soured in his youth by a disappointment in love, of which he spoke but seldom. She lived far away in a town to which he had wandered in the days when his blood ran hot, and they became engaged. Unfortunately, however, Tammy forgot her name, and he never knew the address; so there the affair ended, to his silent grief. He admitted himself, over his snuff-mull of an evening, that he was a very ordinary character, but a certain halo of hor-ror was cast over the whole family by their con-nection with little Joey Sutie, who was pointed at in Thrums as the laddie that whistled when he went past the minister. Joey became a pedlar, and was found dead one raw morning dangling over a high wall within a few miles of Thrums. When climb-ing the dyke his pack had slipped back, the strap round his neck, and choked him.

You could generally tell an Auld Licht in Thrums when you passed him, his dull vacant face wrinkled over a heavy wob. He wore tags of yarn round his trousers beneath the knee, that looked like ostentatious garters, and frequently his jacket of corduroy was put on beneath his waistcoat. If he was too old to carry his load on his back, he wheeled it on a creaking barrow, and when he met a friend they said, " Ay, Jeames," and " Ay, Davit," and then could think of nothing else. At long intervals they passed through the square, disappearing or coming into sight round the town-house which stands on the south side of it, and guards the entrance to a steep brae that leads down and then twists up on its lonely way to the county town. I like to linger over the square, for it was from an upper window in it that I got to know Thrums. On Saturday nights, when the Auld Licht young men came into the square dressed and washed to look at the young women errand-going, and to laugh sometime afterwards to each other, it presented a glare of light; and here even came the cheap jacks and the Fair Circassian, and the showman, who, besides playing " The Mountain Maid and the Shepherd's Bride," exhibited part of the tail of Balaam's ass, the helm of Noah's ark, and the tartan plaid in which Flora McDonald wrapped Prince Charlie. More select entertainment, such as Shuffle Kitty's waxwork, whose motto was, " A rag to pay, and in you go," were given in a hall whose approach was by an outside stair. On the Muckle Friday, the fair for which children storing their pocket money would accumulate sevenpence-halfpenny in less than six months, the square was crammed with gingerbread stalls, bag-pipers, fiddlers, and monstrosities who were gifted with second sight. There was a bearded man, who had neither legs nor arms, and was drawn through the streets in a small cart by four dogs. By looking at you he could see all the clockwork inside, as could a boy who was led about by his mother at the end of a string. Every Friday there was the market, when a dozen ramshackle carts containing vegetables and cheap crockery filled the centre of the square, resting in line on their shafts. A score of farmers' wives or daughters in old-world garments squatted against the town-house within walls of butter on cabbage-leaves, eggs and chickens. Towards evening the voice of the buckie-man shook the square, and rival fish-cadgers, terrible characters who ran races on horseback, screamed libels at each other over a fruiterer's barrow. Then it was time for douce Auld Lichts to go home, draw their stools near the fire, spread their red handkerchiefs over their legs to prevent their trousers getting singed, and read their " Pilgrim's Progress."

In my schoolhouse, however, I seem to see the square most readily in the Scotch mist which so often filled it, loosening the stones and choking the drains. There was then no rattle of rain against my window-sill, nor dancing of diamond drops on the roofs, but blobs of water grew on the panes of glass to reel heavily down them. Then the sodden square would have shed abundant tears if you could have taken it in your hands and wrung it like a dripping cloth. At such a time the square would be empty but for one vegetable cart left in

the care of a lean collie, which, tied to the wheel,
whined and shivered underneath. Pools of water
gather in the coarse sacks, that have been spread
over the potatoes and bundles of greens, which
turn to manure in their lidless barrels. The eyes
of the whimpering dog never leave a black close
over which hangs the sign of the Bull, probably
the refuge of the hawker. At long intervals a
farmer's gig rumbles over the bumpy, ill-paved
square, or a native, with his head buried in his coat,
peeps out of doors, skurries across the way, and
vanishes. Most of the leading shops are here, and
the decorous draper ventures a few yards from the
pavement to scan the sky, or note the effect of his
new arrangement in scarves. Planted against his
door is the butcher, Henders Todd, white-aproned,
and with a knife in his hand, gazing interestedly
at the draper, for a mere man may look at an elder.
The tinsmith brings out his steps, and, mounting
them, stealthily removes the saucepans and pepper-
pots that dangle on a wire above his sign-board.
Pulling to his door he shuts out the foggy light
that showed in his solder-strewn workshop. The
square is deserted again. A bundle of sloppy pars-
ley slips from the hawker's cart and topples over
the wheel in driblets. The puddles in the sacks
overflow and run together. The dog has twisted
his chain round a barrel and yelps sharply. As if
in response comes a rush of other dogs. A terri-

fied fox-terrier tears across the square with half a score of mongrels, the butcher's mastiff and some collies at his heels; he is doubtless a stranger who has insulted them by his glossy coat. For two seconds the square shakes to an invasion of dogs, and then, again, there is only one dog in sight.

No one will admit the Scotch mist. It "looks saft." The tinsmith "wudna wonder but what it was makkin for rain." Tammas Haggart and Pete Lunan dander into sight bareheaded, and have to stretch out their hands to discover what the weather is like. By and by they come to a standstill to discuss the immortality of the soul, and then they are looking silently at the Bull. Neither speaks, but they begin to move toward the inn at the same time, and its door closes on them before they know what they are doing. A few minutes afterwards Jinny Dundas, who is Pete's wife, runs straight for the Bull in her short gown, which is tucked up very high, and emerges with her husband soon afterwards. Jinny is voluble, but Pete says nothing. Tammas follows later, putting his head out at the door first, and looking cautiously about him to see if any one is in sight. Pete is a U. P., and may be left to his fate, but the Auld Licht minister thinks that though it be hard work, Tammas is worth saving.

To the Auld Licht of the past there were three degrees of damnation — auld kirk, play-acting, chapel. Chapel was the name always given to the English Church, of which I am too much an Auld Licht myself to care to write even now. To belong to the chapel was, in Thrums, to be a Roman Catholic, and the boy who flung a clod of earth at the English minister — who called the Sabbath Sunday — or dropped a "divet" down his chimney was held to be in the right way. The only pleasant story Thrums could tell of the chapel was that its steeple once fell. It is surprising that an English church was ever suffered to be built in such a place; though probably the county gentry had something to do with it. They travelled about too much to be good men. Small though Thrums used to be, it had four kirks in all before the Disruption, and then another, which split into two immediately afterwards. The spire of the parish church, known as the auld kirk, commands a view of the square, from which the entrance to the kirkyard would be visible, if it were not hidden by the town-house. The kirkyard has long been crammed, and is not now in use, but the church is sufficiently large to hold nearly all the congregations in Thrums. Just at the gate lived Pete Todd, the father of Sam'l, a man of whom the Auld Lichts had reason to be proud. Pete was an every-day man at ordinary times, and was even said, when his wife, who had been long ill, died, to have clapped his hands and exclaimed, "Hip, hip, hurrah!" adding only as an afterthought, "The Lord's will be done." But midsummer was his great opportunity. Then took place the rouping of the seats in the parish church. The scene was the kirk itself, and the seats being put up to auction were knocked down to the highest bidder. This sometimes led to the breaking of the peace. Every person was present who was at all particular as to where he sat, and an auctioneer was engaged for the day. He rouped the kirk-seats like potato-drills, beginning by asking for a bid. Every seat was put up to auction separately; for some were much more run after than others, and the men were instructed by their wives what to bid for. Often the women joined in, and as they bid excitedly against each other the church rang with opprobrious epithets. A man would come to the roup late, and learn that the seat he wanted had been knocked down. He maintained that he had been unfairly treated, or denounced the local laird to whom the seat-rents went. If he did not get the seat he would leave the kirk. Then the woman who had forestalled him wanted to know what he meant by glaring at her so, and the auction was interrupted. Another member would "thrip down the throat" of the auctioneer that he had a right to his former seat if he continued to pay the same price for it. The auctioneer was screamed at for favouring his friends, and at times the roup became so noisy that men and women had to be forcibly ejected. Then was Pete's chance. Hovering at the gate, he caught the angry people on their way home and took them into his workshop by an outside stair. There he assisted them in denouncing the parish kirk, with the view of getting them to forswear it. Pete made a good many Auld Lichts in his time out of unpromising material.

Sights were to be witnessed in the parish church at times that could not have been made more impressive by the Auld Lichts themselves. Here sinful women were grimly taken to task by the minister, who, having thundered for a time against adultery in general, called upon one sinner in particular to stand forth. She had to step forward into a pew near the pulpit, where, alone and friendless, and stared at by the congregation, she cowered in tears beneath his denunciations. In that seat she had to remain during the forenoon service. She returned home alone, and had to come back alone to her solitary seat in the afternoon. All day no one dared speak to her. She was as much an object of contumely as the thieves and smugglers whom, in the end of last century, it was the privilege of Feudal Bailie Wood (as he was called) to whip round the square.

It is nearly twenty years since the gardeners

had their last "walk" in Thrums, and they survived all the other benefit societies that walked
once every summer. There was a "weavers'
walk" and five or six others, the "women's walk"
being the most picturesque. These were proces-
sions of the members of benefit societies through
the square and wynds, and all the women walked
in white, to the number of a hundred or more,
behind the Tilliedrum band, Thrums having in
those days no band of its own.

From the north-west corner of the square a
narrow street sets off, jerking this way and that
as if uncertain what point to make for. Here
lurks the post-office, which had once the reputation of being as crooked in its ways as the street
itself.

A railway line runs into Thrums now. The
sensational days of the post-office were when the
letters were conveyed officially in a creaking old
cart from Tilliedrum. The "pony" had seen
better days than the cart, and always looked as if
he were just on the point of succeeding in running away from it. Hooky Crewe was driver;
so-called because an iron hook was his substitute
for a right arm: Robbie Proctor, the blacksmith,
made the hook and fixed it in. Crewe suffered
from rheumatism, and when he felt it coming on
he stayed at home. Sometimes his cart came un-
done in a snowdrift; when Hooky, extricated

from the fragments by some chance wayfarer, was deposited with his mail-bag (of which he always kept a grip by the hook) in a farm-house. It was his boast that his letters always reached their destination eventually. They might be a long time about it, but "slow *and* sure" was his motto. Hooky emphasized his "slow *and* sure" by taking a snuff. He was a godsend to the postmistress, for to his failings or the infirmities of his gig were charged all delays.

At the time I write of, the posting of the letter took as long and was as serious an undertaking as the writing. That means a good deal, for many of the letters were written to dictation by the Thrums schoolmaster, Mr. Fleemister, who belonged to the Auld Kirk. He was one of the few persons in the community who looked upon the despatch of his letters by the postmistress as his right, and not a favour on her part; there was a long-standing feud between them accordingly. After a few tumblers of Widow Stables's treacle-beer — in the concoction of which she was the acknowledged mistress for miles around — the schoolmaster would sometimes go the length of hinting that he could get the postmistress dismissed any day. This mighty power seemed to rest on a knowledge of "steamed" letters. Thrums had a high respect for the schoolmaster; but among themselves the weavers agreed that, even if he did write

20

to the Government, Lizzie Harrison, the postmistress, would refuse to transmit the letter. The more shrewd ones among us kept friends with both parties; for, unless you could write "writ-hand," you could not compose a letter without the schoolmaster's assistance; and, unless Lizzie was so courteous as to send it to its destination, it might lie — or so it was thought — much too long in the box. A letter addressed by the schoolmaster found great disfavour in Lizzie's eyes. You might explain to her that you had merely called in his assistance because you were a poor hand at writing yourself, but that was held no excuse. Some addressed their own envelopes with much labour, and sought to palm off the whole as their handiwork. It reflects on the postmistress somewhat that she had generally found them out by next day, when, if in a specially vixenish mood, she did not hesitate to upbraid them for their perfidy.

To post a letter you did not merely saunter to the post-office and drop it into the box. The cautious correspondent first went into the shop and explained to Lizzie how matters stood. She kept what she called a bookseller's shop as well as the post-office; but the supply of books corresponded exactly to the lack of demand for them, and her chief trade was in nicknacks, from marbles and money-boxes up to concertinas. If he found the postmistress in an amiable mood, which was only now and then, the caller led up craftily to the object of his visit. Having discussed the weather and the potato-disease, he explained that his sister Mary, whom Lizzie would remember, had married a fishmonger in Dundee. The fishmonger had lately started on himself and was doing well. They had four children. The youngest had had a severe attack of measles. No news had been got of Mary for twelve months; and Annie, his other sister, who lived in Thrums, had been at him of late for not writing. So he had written a few lines; and, in fact, he had the letter with him. The letter was then produced, and examined by the postmistress. If the address was in the schoolmaster's handwriting, she professed her inability to read it. Was this a *t* or an *l* or an *i*? was that a *b* or a *d*? This was a cruel revenge on Lizzie's part; for the sender of the letter was completely at her mercy. The schoolmaster's name being tabooed in her presence, he was unable to explain that the writing was not his own; and as for deciding between the *t*'s and *l*'s, he could not do it. Eventually he would be directed to put the letter into the box. They would do their best with it, Lizzie said, but in a voice that suggested how little hope she had of her efforts to decipher it proving successful.

There was an opinion among some of the people that the letter should not be stamped by the sender. The proper thing to do was to drop a penny for the stamp into the box along with the letter, and then Lizzie would see that it was all right. Lizzie's acquaintance with the handwriting of every person in the place who could write gave her a great advantage. You would perhaps drop into her shop some day to make a purchase, when she would calmly produce a letter you had posted several days before. In explanation she would tell you that you had not put a stamp on it, or that she suspected there was money in it, or that you had addressed it to the wrong place. I remember an old man, a relative of my own, who happened for once in his life to have several letters to post at one time. The circumstance was so out of the common that he considered it only reasonable to make Lizzie a small present.

Perhaps the postmistress was belied; but if she did not " steam " the letters and confide their tit-bits to favoured friends of her own sex, it is difficult to see how all the gossip got out. The schoolmaster once played an unmanly trick on her, with the view of catching her in the act. He was a bachelor who had long been given up by all the maids in the town. One day, however, he wrote a letter to an imaginary lady in the county-town, asking her to be his, and going into full particulars about his income, his age, and his prospects. A male friend in the secret, at the other end, was to reply, in a lady's handwriting, accepting him, and

also giving personal particulars. The first letter
was written; and an answer arrived in due course
— two days, the schoolmaster said, after date. No
other person knew of this scheme for the undoing
of the postmistress, yet in a very short time the
schoolmaster's coming marriage was the talk of
Thrums. Everybody became suddenly aware of
the lady's name, of her abode, and of the sum of
money she was to bring her husband. It was even
noised abroad that the schoolmaster had represented his age as a good ten years less than it was.
Then the schoolmaster divulged everything. To
his mortification, he was not quite believed. All
the proof he could bring forward to support his
story was this : that time would show whether he got
married or not. Foolish man! this argument was
met by another, which was accepted at once. The
lady had jilted the schoolmaster. Whether this
explanation came from the post-office, who shall
say? But so long as he lived the schoolmaster was
twitted about the lady who threw him over. He
took his revenge in two ways. He wrote and
posted letters exceedingly abusive of the postmistress. The matter might be libellous; but then,
as he pointed out, she would incriminate herself
if she "brought him up" about it. Probably
Lizzie felt his other insult more. By publishing
his suspicions of her on every possible occasion he
got a few people to seal their letters. So bitter

was his feeling against her that he was even willing to supply the wax.

They know all about post-offices in Thrums now, and even jeer at the telegraph-boy's uniform. In the old days they gathered round him when he was seen in the street, and escorted him to his destination in triumph. That, too, was after Lizzie had gone the way of all the earth. But perhaps they are not even yet as knowing as they think themselves. I was told the other day that one of them took out a postal order, meaning to send the money to a relative, and kept the order as a receipt.

I have said that the town is sometimes full of snow. One frosty Saturday, seven years ago, I trudged into it from the schoolhouse, and on the Monday morning we could not see Thrums anywhere.

I was in one of the proud two-storied houses in the place, and could have shaken hands with my friends without from the upper windows. To get out of doors you had to walk upstairs. The outlook was a sea of snow fading into white hills and sky with the quarry standing out red and ragged to the right like a rock in the ocean. The Auld Licht manse was gone, but had left its garden-trees behind, their lean branches soft with snow. Roofs were humps in the white blanket. The spire of the Established Kirk stood up cold and stiff, like a monument to the buried inhabitants.

25

Those of the natives who had taken the precaution of conveying spades into their houses the night before, which is my plan at the schoolhouse, dug themselves out. They hobbled cautiously over the snow, sometimes sinking into it to their knees, when they stood still and slowly took in the situation. It had been snowing more or less for a week, but in a commonplace kind of way, and they had gone to bed thinking all was well. This night the snow must have fallen as if the heavens had opened up, determined to shake themselves free of it for ever.

The man who first came to himself and saw what was to be done was young Henders Ramsay. Henders had no fixed occupation, being but an " orra man " about the place, and the best thing known of him is that his mother's sister was a Baptist. He feared God, man, nor the minister; and all the learning he had was obtained from assiduous study of a grocer's window. But for one brief day he had things his own way in the town, or, speaking strictly, on the top of it. With a spade, a broom, and a pickaxe, which sat lightly on his broad shoulders (he was not even back-bent, and that showed him no respectable weaver), Henders delved his way to the nearest house, which formed one of a row, and addressed the inmates down the chimney. They had already been clearing it at the other end, or his words would have been choked. "You're snawed up, Davit," cried Henders, in a voice that was entirely businesslike; "hae ye a spade?" A conversation ensued up and down this unusual channel of communication. The unlucky householder, taking no thought of the morrow, was without a spade. But if Henders would clear away the snow from his door he would be "varra obleeged." Henders, however, had to come to terms first. "The chairge is saxpence, Davit," he shouted. Then a haggling ensued. Henders must be neighbourly. A plate of broth, now — or, say, twopence. But Henders was obdurate. "I'se nae time to argy-bargy wi' ye, Davit. Gin ye're no willin' to say saxpence, I'm aff to Will'um Pyatt's. He's buried too." So the victim had to make up his mind to one of two things: he must either say saxpence or remain where he was.

If Henders was "promised," he took good care that no snowed-up inhabitant should perjure himself. He made his way to a window first, and, clearing the snow from the top of it, pointed out that he could not conscientiously proceed further until the debt had been paid. "Money doon," he cried, as soon as he reached a pane of glass; or, "Come awa wi' my saxpence noo."

The belief that this day had not come to Henders unexpectedly was borne out by the method of the crafty callant. His charges varied from sixpence to half-a-crown, according to the wealth and status of his victims; and when, later on, there were rivals in the snow, he had the discrimination to reduce his minimum fee to threepence. He had the honour of digging out three ministers at one shilling, one and threepence, and two shillings respectively.

Half a dozen times within the next fortnight the town was reburied in snow. This generally happened in the night-time; but the inhabitants were not to be caught unprepared again. Spades stood ready to their hands in the morning, and they fought their way above ground without Henders Ramsay's assistance. To clear the snow from the narrow wynds and pends, however, was a task not to be attempted; and the Auld Lichts, at least, rested content when enough light got into their workshops to let them see where their looms stood. Wading through beds of snow they did not much mind; but they wondered what would happen to their houses when the thaw came.

The thaw was slow in coming. Snow during the night and several degrees of frost by day were what Thrums began to accept as a revised order of nature. Vainly the Thrums doctor, whose practice extends into the glens, made repeated attempts to reach his distant patients, twice driving so far into the dreary waste that he could neither go on nor turn back. A ploughman who contrived to gallop ten miles for him did not get home for a week. Between the town, which is nowadays an agricultural centre of some importance, and the outlying farms communication was cut off for a month; and I heard subsequently of one farmer who did not see a human being, unconnected with his own farm, for seven weeks. The schoolhouse, which I managed to reach only two days behind time, was closed for a fortnight, and even in Thrums there was only a sprinkling of scholars.

On Sundays the feeling between the different denominations ran high, and the middling good folk who did not go to church counted those who did. In the Established Church there was a sparse gathering, who waited in vain for the minister. After a time it got abroad that a flag of distress was flying from the manse, and then they saw that the minister was storm-stayed. An office-bearer offered to conduct service; but the others present thought they had done their duty and went home. The U. P. bell did not ring at all, and the kirk gates were not opened. The Free Kirk did bravely, however. The attendance in the forenoon amounted to seven, including the minister; but in the afternoon there was a turn-out of upwards of fifty. How much denominational competition had to do with this, none can say; but the general opinion was that this muster to after-

noon service was a piece of vainglory. Next
Sunday all the kirks were on their mettle, and,
though the snow was drifting the whole day, services were general. It was felt that after the action
of the Free Kirk the Establisheds and the U. P.'s
must show what they too were capable of. So,
when the bells rang at eleven o'clock and two,
church-goers began to pour out of every close. If
I remember aright, the victory lay with the U. P.'s
by two women and a boy. Of course the Auld
Lichts mustered in as great force as ever. The
other kirks never dreamt of competing with them.
What was regarded as a judgment on the Free
Kirk for its boastfulness of spirit on the preceding
Sunday happened during the forenoon. While
the service was taking place a huge clod of snow
slipped from the roof and fell right against the
church door. It was some time before the pris-
oners could make up their minds to leave by the
windows. What the Auld Lichts would have
done in a similar predicament I cannot even conjecture.

That was the first warning of the thaw. It froze
again; there was more snow; the thaw began in
earnest; and then the streets were a sight to see.
There was no traffic to turn the snow to slush, and,
where it had not been piled up in walls a few feet
from the houses, it remained in the narrow ways
till it became a lake. It tried to escape through

doorways, when it sank slowly into the floors. Gentle breezes created a ripple on its surface, and strong winds lifted it into the air and flung it against the houses. It undermined the heaps of clotted snow till they tottered like icebergs and fell to pieces. Men made their way through it on stilts. Had a frost followed, the result would have been appalling; but there was no more frost that winter. A fortnight passed before the place looked itself again, and even then congealed snow stood doggedly in the streets, while the country roads were like newly ploughed fields after rain. The heat from large fires soon penetrated through roofs of slate and thatch; and it was quite a common thing for a man to be flattened to the ground by a slithering of snow from above just as he opened his door. But it had seldom more than ten feet to fall. Most interesting of all was the novel sensation experienced as Thrums began to assume its familiar aspect, and objects so long buried that they had been half forgotten came back to view and use.

Storm-stayed shows used to emphasize the severity of a Thrums winter. As the name indicates, these were gatherings of travelling booths in the winter-time. Half a century ago the country was overrun by itinerant showmen, who went their different ways in summer, but formed little colonies in the cold weather, when they pitched their tents in any empty field or disused quarry and huddled

together for the sake of warmth : not that they got
much of it. Not more than five winters ago we
had a storm-stayed show on a small scale ; but nowadays the farmers are less willing to give these
wanderers a camping-place, and the people are less
easily drawn to the entertainments provided, by
fife and drum. The colony hung together until it
was starved out, when it trailed itself elsewhere. I
have often seen it forming. The first arrival would
be what was popularly known as "Sam'l Mann's
Tumbling-Booth," with its tumblers, jugglers,
sword-swallowers, and balancers. This travelling
show visited us regularly twice a year : once in
summer for the Muckle Friday, when the per-
formers were gay and stout, and even the horses
had flesh on their bones ; and again in the "back-
end " of the year, when cold and hunger had taken
the blood from their faces, and the scraggy dogs
that whined at their side were lashed for licking the
paint off the caravans. While the storm-stayed
show was in the vicinity the villages suffered from
an invasion of these dogs. Nothing told more truly
the dreadful tale of the showman's life in winter.
Sam'l Mann's was a big show, and half a dozen
smaller ones, most of which were familiar to us,
crawled in its wake. Others heard of its whereabouts and came in from distant parts. There was
the well-known Gubbins with his "A' the World
in a Box :" a halfpenny peepshow, in which all the

world was represented by Joseph and his Brethren (with pit and coat), the bombardment of Copenhagen, the Battle of the Nile, Daniel in the Den of Lions, and Mount Etna in eruption. "Aunt Maggy's Whirligig" could be enjoyed on payment of an old pair of boots, a collection of rags, or the like. Besides these and other shows, there were the wandering minstrels, most of whom were "Waterloo veterans" wanting arms or a leg. I remember one whose arms had been "smashed by a thunderbolt at Jamaica." Queer bent old dames, who superintended "lucky bags" or told fortunes, supplied the uncanny element, but hesitated to call themselves witches, for there can still be seen near Thrums the pool where these unfortunates used to be drowned, and in the session book of the Glen Quharity kirk can be read an old minute announcing that on a certain Sabbath there was no preaching because "the minister was away at the burning of a witch." To the storm-stayed shows came the gypsies in great numbers. Claypots (which is a corruption of Claypits) was their headquarters near Thrums, and it is still sacred to their memory. It was a clachan of miserable little huts built entirely of clay from the dreary and sticky pit in which they had been flung together. A shapeless hole on one side was the doorway, and a little hole, stuffed with straw in winter, the window. Some of the remnants of these hovels still stand. Their occupants, though they went by the name of gypsies among themselves, were known to the weavers as the Claypots beggars; and their King was Jimmy Pawse. His regal dignity gave Jimmy the right to seek alms first when he chose to do so; thus he got the cream of a place before his subjects set to work. He was rather foppish in his dress; generally affecting a suit of grey cloth with showy metal buttons on it, and a broad blue bonnet. His wife was a little body like himself; and when they went a-begging, Jimmy with a meal-bag for alms on his back, she always took her husband's arm. Jimmy was the legal adviser of his subjects; his decision was considered final on all questions, and he guided them in their courtships as well as on their death-beds. He christened their children and officiated at their weddings, marrying them over the tongs.

The storm-stayed show attracted old and young — to looking on from the outside. In the day-time the wagons and tents presented a dreary appearance, sunk in snow, the dogs shivering between the wheels, and but little other sign of life visible. When dusk came the lights were lit, and the drummer and fifer from the booth of tumblers were sent into the town to entice an audience. They marched quickly through the nipping, windy streets, and then returned with two or three score of men, women, and children, plunging through the snow or mud at their heavy heels. It was

THRUMS

Orpheus fallen from his high estate. What a mockery the glare of the lamps and the capers of the mountebanks were, and how satisfied were we to enjoy it all without going inside. I hear the "Waterloo veterans" still, and remember their patriotic outbursts:

On the sixteenth day of June, brave boys, while cannon loud did roar,
We being short of cavalry they pressed on us full sore ;
But British steel soon made them yield, though our numbers was but few,
And death or victory was the word on the plains of Waterloo.

The storm-stayed shows often found it easier to sink to rest in a field than to leave it. For weeks at a time they were snowed up, sufficiently to prevent any one from Thrums going near them, though not sufficiently to keep the pallid mummers indoors. That would in many cases have meant starvation. They managed to fight their way through storm and snowdrift to the high road and thence to the town, where they got meal and sometimes broth. The tumblers and jugglers used occasionally to hire an out-house in the town at these times — you may be sure they did not pay for it in advance — and give performances there. It is a curious thing, but true, that our herd-boys and others were sometimes struck with the stage-fever. Thrums lost boys to the showmen even in winter.

On the whole, the farmers and the people generally were wonderfully long-suffering with these wanderers, who I believe were more honest than was to be expected. They stole, certainly; but seldom did they steal anything more valuable than turnips. Sam'l Mann himself flushed proudly over the effect his show once had on an irate farmer. The farmer appeared in the encampment, whip in hand and furious. They must get off his land before nightfall. The crafty showman, however, prevailed upon him to take a look at the acrobats, and he enjoyed the performance so much that he offered to let them stay until the end of the week. Before that time came there was such a fall of snow that departure was out of the question; and it is to the farmer's credit that he sent Sam'l a bag of meal to tide him and his actors over the storm.

There were times when the showmen made a tour of the bothies, where they slung their poles and ropes and gave their poor performances to audiences that were not critical. The bothy being strictly the "man's" castle, the farmer never interfered; indeed, he was sometimes glad to see the show. Every other weaver in Thrums used to have a son a ploughman, and it was the men from the bothies who filled the square on the muckly. "Hands" are not huddled together nowadays in squalid barns more like cattle than men and women, but bothies in the neighbourhood of Thrums are not yet things of the past. Many a ploughman delves his way to and from them still in all weathers, when the snow is on the ground; at the time of "hairst," and when the turnip "shaws" have just forced themselves through the earth, looking like straight rows of green needles. Here is a picture of a bothy of to-day that I visited recently. Over the door there is a water-spout that has given way, and as I entered I got a rush of rain down my neck. The passage was so small that one could easily have stepped from the doorway on to the ladder standing against the wall, which was there in lieu of a staircase. "Up-stairs" was a mere garret, where a man could not stand erect even in the centre. It was entered by a square hole in the ceiling, at present closed by a clap-door in no way dissimilar to the trap-doors on a theatre stage. I climbed into this garret, which is at present used as a store-room for agri-cultural odds and ends. At harvest-time, however, it is inhabited — full to overflowing. A few de-cades ago as many as fifty labourers engaged for the harvest had to be housed in the farm out-houses on beds of straw. There was no help for it, and men and women had to congregate in these barns together. Up as early as five in the morning, they were generally dead tired by night; and, miserable though this system of herding them together was, they took it like stoics, and their very number served as a moral safeguard. Nowadays the harvest is gathered in so quickly, and machinery does so much that used to be done by hand, that this crowding of labourers together, which was the bothy system at its worst, is nothing like what it was. As many as six or eight men, however, are put up in the garret referred to during "hairst"-time, and the female labourers have to make the best of it in the barn. There is no doubt that on many farms the two sexes have still at this busy time to herd together even at night.

The bothy was but scantily furnished, though it consisted of two rooms. In the one, which was used almost solely as a sleeping apartment, there was no furniture to speak of, beyond two closet beds, and its bumpy earthen floor gave it a cheerless look. The other, which had a single bed, was floored with wood. It was not badly lit by two very small windows that faced each other, and, besides several stools, there was a long form against one of the walls. A bright fire of peat and coal — nothing in the world makes such a cheerful red fire as this combination — burned beneath a big kettle ("boiler" they called it), and there was a "press" or cupboard containing a fair assortment of cooking utensils. Of these some belonged to the bothy, while others were the private property of the tenants. A tin "pan" and "pitcher" of water stood near the door, and the table in the middle of the room was covered with oilcloth.

Four men and a boy inhabited this bothy, and the rain had driven them all indoors. In better weather they spend the leisure of the evening at the game of quoits, which is the standard pastime among Scottish ploughmen. They fish the neighbouring streams, too, and have burn-trout for supper several times a week. When I entered, two of them were sitting by the fire playing draughts, or, as they called it, "the dam-brod." The dambrod is the Scottish labourer's billiards; and he often attains to a remarkable proficiency at the game. Wylie, the champion draught-player, was once a herd-boy; and wonderful stories are current in all bothies of the times when his master called him into the farm-parlour to show his skill. A third man, who seemed the elder by quite twenty years, was at the window reading a newspaper; and I got no shock when I saw that it was the *Saturday Review*, which he and a labourer on an adjoining farm took in weekly between them. There was a copy of a local newspaper — the *People's Journal* — also lying about, and some books, including one of Darwin's. These were all the property of this man, however, who did the reading for the bothy.

They did all the cooking for themselves, living

largely on milk.   In the old days, which the senior
could remember, porridge was so universally the
morning meal that they called it by that name instead of breakfast.   They still breakfast on porridge, but often take tea " above it."   Generally
milk is taken with the porridge; but " porter " or
stout in a bowl is no uncommon substitute.   Potatoes at twelve o'clock — seldom " brose " nowadays — are the staple dinner dish, and the tinned
meats have become very popular.   There are
bothies where each man makes his own food; but
of course the more satisfactory plan is for them to
club together.   Sometimes they get their food in
the farm-kitchen; but this is only when there are
few of them and the farmer and his family do not
think it beneath them to dine with the men.   Broth,
too, may be made in the kitchen and sent down to
the bothy.   At harvest-time the workers take their
food in the fields, when great quantities of milk
are provided.   There is very little beer drunk, and
whisky is only consumed in privacy.

Life in the bothies is not, I should say, so lonely
as life at the schoolhouse, for the hands have at
least each other's company.   The hawker visits
them frequently still, though the itinerant tailor,
once a familiar figure, has almost vanished.   Their
great place of congregating is still some country
smiddy, which is also their frequent meeting-place
when bent on black-fishing.   The flare of the

black-fisher's torch still attracts salmon to their
death in the rivers near Thrums; and you may
hear in the glens on a dark night the rattle of the
spears on the wet stones. Twenty or thirty years
ago, however, the sport was much more common.
After the farmer had gone to bed, some half-dozen
ploughmen and a few other poachers from Thrums
would set out for the meeting-place.

The smithy on these occasions must have been
a weird sight; though one did not mark that at
the time. The poacher crept from the darkness
into the glaring smithy light; for in country parts
the anvil might sometimes be heard clanging at all
hours of the night. As a rule, every face was
blackened; and it was this, I suppose, rather than
the fact that dark nights were chosen that gave the
gangs the name of black-fishers. Other disguises
were resorted to; one of the commonest being to
change clothes or to turn your corduroys outside
in. The country-folk of those days were more su-
perstitious than they are now, and it did not take
much to turn the black-fishers back. There was
not a barn or byre in the district that had not its
horseshoe over the door. Another popular device
for frightening away witches and fairies was to
hang bunches of garlic about the farms. I have
known a black-fishing expedition stopped because
a "yellow yite," or yellowhammer, hovered round
the gang when they were setting out. Still more

ominous was the "péat" when it appeared with one or three companions. An old rhyme about this bird runs — "One is joy, two is grief, three's a bridal, four is death." Such snatches of superstition are still to be heard amidst the gossip of a north-country smithy.

Each black-fisher brought his own spear and torch, both more or less home-made. The spears were in many cases "gully-knives," fastened to staves with twine and resin, called "rozet." The torches were very rough-and-ready things — rope and tar, or even rotten roots dug from broken trees — in fact, anything that would flare. The black-fishers seldom journeyed far from home, confining themselves to the rivers within a radius of three or four miles. There were many reasons for this: one of them being that the hands had to be at their work on the farm by five o'clock in the morning; another, that so they poached and let poach. Except when in spate, the river I specially refer to offered no attractions to the black-fishers. Heavy rains, however, swell it much more quickly than most rivers into a turbulent rush of water; the part of it affected by the black-fishers being banked in with rocks that prevent the water's spreading. Above these rocks, again, are heavy green banks, from which stunted trees grow aslant across the river. The effect is fearsome at some points where the trees run into each other, as it

were, from opposite banks. However, the black-
fishers thought nothing of these things. They
took a turnip lantern with them — that is, a lantern hollowed out of a turnip, with a piece of candle inside — but no lights were shown on the road.
Every one knew his way to the river blindfold;
so that the darker the night the better. On reaching the water there was a pause. One or two of
the gang climbed the banks to discover if any bailiffs were on the watch; while the others sat down,
and with the help of the turnip lantern "busked"
their spears; in other words, fastened on the steel
— or, it might be, merely pieces of rusty iron
sharpened into a point at home — to the staves.
Some had them busked before they set out, but
that was not considered prudent; for of course
there was always a risk of meeting spoil-sports on
the way, to whom the spears would tell a tale that
could not be learned from ordinary staves. Nevertheless little time was lost. Five or six of the
gang waded into the water, torch in one hand and
spear in the other; and the object now was to
catch some salmon with the least possible delay,
and hurry away. Windy nights were good for
the sport, and I can still see the river lit up with
the lumps of light that a torch makes in a high
wind. The torches, of course, were used to at-
tract the fish, which came swimming to the sheen,
and were then speared. As little noise as possible

was made; but though the men bit their lips instead of crying out when they missed their fish, there was a continuous ring of their weapons on the stones, and every irrepressible imprecation was echoed up and down the black glen. Two or three of the gang were told off to land the salmon, and they had to work smartly and deftly. They kept by the side of the spearsman, and the moment he struck a fish they grabbed at it with their hands. When the spear had a barb there was less chance of the fish's being lost; but often this was not the case, and probably not more than two-thirds of the salmon speared were got safely to the bank. The takes of course varied; sometimes, indeed, the black-fishers returned home empty-handed.

Encounters with the bailiffs were not infrequent, though they seldom took place at the water's edge. When the poachers were caught in the act, and had their blood up with the excitement of the sport, they were ugly customers. Spears were used and heads were broken. Struggles even took place in the water, when there was always a chance of somebody's being drowned. Where the bailiffs gave the black-fishers an opportunity of escaping without a fight it was nearly always taken; the booty being left behind. As a rule, when the " water-watchers," as the bailiffs were sometimes called, had an inkling of what was to take place, they reinforced themselves with a constable or two and waited on the road to catch the poachers on their way home. One black-fisher, a noted character, was nicknamed the "Deil o' Glen Quharity." He was said to have gone to the houses of the bailiffs and offered to sell them the fish stolen from the streams over which they kept guard. The "Deil" was never imprisoned — partly, perhaps, because he was too eccentric to be taken seriously.

CHAPTER III

THE AULD LICHT KIRK

ONE Sabbath day in the beginning of the century the Auld Licht minister at Thrums walked out of his battered, ramshackle, earthen-floored kirk with a following and never returned. The last words he uttered in it were: "Follow me to the commonty, all you persons who want to hear the Word of God properly preached; and James Duphie and his two sons will answer for this on the Day of Judgment." The congregation, which belonged to the body who seceded from the Established Church a hundred and fifty years ago, had split, and as the New Lights (now the U. P.'s) were in the majority, the Old Lights, with the minister at their head, had to retire to the commonty (or common) and hold service in the open air until they had saved up money for a church. They kept possession, however, of the white manse among the trees. Their kirk has but a cluster of members now, most of them old and done, but each is equal to a dozen ordinary church-goers, and there have been men and women among

46

them on whom the memory loves to linger. For forty years they have been dying out, but their cold, stiff pews still echo the Psalms of David, and the Auld Licht kirk will remain open so long as it has one member and a minister.

The church stands round the corner from the square, with only a large door to distinguish it from the other building in the short street. Children who want to do a brave thing hit this door with their fists, when there is no one near, and then run away scared. The door, however, is sacred to the memory of a white-haired old lady who, not so long ago, used to march out of the kirk and remain on the pavement until the psalm which had just been given out was sung. Of Thrums's pavement it may here be said that when you come, even to this day, to a level slab you feel reluctant to leave it. The old lady was Mistress (which is Miss) Tibbie McQuhatty, and she nearly split the Auld Licht kirk over "run line." This conspicuous innovation was introduced by Mr. Dishart, the minister, when he was young and audacious. The old, reverent custom in the kirk was for the precentor to read out the psalm a line at a time. Having then sung that line he read out the next one, led the singing of it, and so worked his way on to line three. Where run line holds, however, the psalm is read out first, and forthwith sung. This is not only a flighty way of doing things, which may lead to greater scandals, but has its practical disadvantages, for the precentor always starts singing in advance of the congregation (Auld Lichts never being able to begin to do anything all at once), and, increasing the distance with every line, leaves them hopelessly behind at the finish. Miss McQuhatty protested against this change, as meeting the devil half way, but the minister carried his point, and ever after that she rushed ostentatiously from the church the moment a psalm was given out, and remained behind the door until the singing was finished, when she returned, with a rustle, to her seat. Run line had on her the effect of the reading of the Riot Act. Once some men, capable of anything, held the door from the outside, and the congregation heard Tibbie rampaging in the passage. Bursting into the kirk she called the office-bearers to her assistance, whereupon the minister in miniature raised his voice and demanded the why and wherefore of the ungodly disturbance. Great was the hubbub, but the door was fast, and a compromise had to be arrived at. The old lady consented for once to stand in the passage, but not without pressing her hands to her ears. You may smile at Tibbie, but ah! I know what she was at a sick bedside. I have seen her when the hard look had gone from her eyes, and it would ill become me to smile too.

As with all the churches in Thrums, care had

48

been taken to make the Auld Licht one much too large. The stair to the "laft" or gallery, which was originally little more than a ladder, is ready for you as soon as you enter the doorway, but it is best to sit in the body of the kirk. The plate for collections is inside the church, so that the whole congregation can give a guess at what you give. If it is something very stingy or very liberal, all Thrums knows of it within a few hours; indeed, this holds good of all the churches, especially perhaps of the Free one, which has been called the bawbee kirk, because so many halfpennies find their way into the plate. On Saturday nights the Thrums shops are besieged for coppers by housewives of all denominations, who would as soon think of dropping a threepenny bit into the plate as of giving nothing. Tammy Todd had a curious way of tipping his penny into the Auld Licht plate while still keeping his hand to his side. He did it much as a boy fires a marble, and there was quite a talk in the congregation the first time he missed. A devout plan was to carry your penny in your hand all the way to church, but to appear to take it out of your pocket on entering, and some plumped it down noisily like men paying their way. I believe old Snecky Hobart, who was a canty stock but obstinate, once dropped a penny into the plate and took out a halfpenny as change, but the only untoward thing that happened to the plate was once when the lassie from the farm of Curly Bog capsized it in passing. Mr. Dishart, who was always a ready man, introduced something into his sermon that day about women's dress, which every one hoped Chirsty Lundy, the lassie in question, would remember. Nevertheless, the minister sometimes came to a sudden stop himself when passing from the vestry to the pulpit. The passage being narrow, his rigging would catch in a pew as he sailed down the aisle. Even then, however, Mr. Dishart remembered that he was not as other men.

White is not a religious colour, and the walls of the kirk were of a dull grey. A cushion was allowed to the manse pew, but merely as a symbol of office, and this was the only pew in the church that had a door. It was and is the pew nearest to the pulpit on the minister's right, and one day it contained a bonnet which Mr. Dishart's predecessor preached at for one hour and ten minutes. From the pulpit, which was swaddled in black, the minister had a fine sweep of all the congregation except those in the back pews downstairs, who were lost in the shadow of the laft. Here sat Whinny Webster, so called because, having an inexplicable passion against them, he devoted his life to the extermination of whins. Whinny for years ate peppermint lozenges with impunity in his back seat, safe in the certainty that the minister, however much he might try, could not possibly see him. But his day came. One afternoon the kirk smelt of peppermints, and Mr. Dishart could rebuke no one, for the defaulter was not in sight. Whinny's cheek was working up and down in quiet enjoyment of its lozenge, when he started, noticing that the preaching had stopped. Then he heard a sepulchral voice say "Charles Webster!" Whinny's eyes turned to the pulpit, only part of which was visible to him, and to his horror they encountered the minister's head coming down the stairs. This took place after I had ceased to attend the Auld Licht kirk regularly; but I am told that as Whinny gave one wild scream the peppermint dropped from his mouth. The minister had got him by leaning over the pulpit door until, had he given himself only another inch, his feet would have gone into the air. As for Whinny he became a Godfearing man.

The most uncanny thing about the kirk was the precentor's box beneath the pulpit. Three Auld Licht ministers I have known, but I can only conceive one precentor. Lang Tammas's box was much too small for him. Since his disappearance from Thrums I believe they have paid him the compliment of enlarging it for a smaller man—no doubt with the feeling that Tammas alone could look like a Christian in it. Like the whole congregation, of course, he had to stand during the prayers—the first of which averaged half an hour in length. If he stood erect his head and shoulders vanished beneath funereal trappings, when he seemed decapitated, and if he stretched his neck the pulpit tottered. He looked like the pillar on which it rested, or he balanced it on his head like a baker's tray. Sometimes he leaned forward as reverently as he could, and then, with his long lean arms dangling over the side of his box, he might have been a suit of "blacks" hung up to dry. Once I was talking with Cree Queery in a sober, respectable manner, when all at once a light broke out on his face. I asked him what he was laughing at, and he said it was at Lang Tammas. He got grave again when I asked him what there was in Lang Tammas to smile at, and admitted that he could not tell me. However, I have always been of opinion that the thought of the precentor in his box gave Cree a fleeting sense of humour.

Tammas and Hendry Munn were the two paid officials of the church, Hendry being kirk-officer; but poverty was among the few points they had in common. The precentor was a cobbler, though he never knew it, shoemaker being the name in those parts, and his dwelling-room was also his workshop. There he sat in his "brot," or apron, from early morning to far on to midnight, and contrived to make his six or eight shillings a week. I have often sat with him in the darkness that his "cruizey" lamp could not pierce, while his mutterings to himself of "ay, ay, yes, umpha, oh ay,

ay man," came as regularly and monotonously
as the tick of his " wag-at-the-wa' " clock. Hendry
and he were paid no fixed sum for their services
in the Auld Licht kirk, but once a year there was
a collection for each of them, and so they jogged
along. Though not the only kirk-officer of my
time Hendry made the most lasting impression.
He was, I think, the only man in Thrums who
did not quake when the minister looked at him.
A wild story, never authenticated, says that Hendry
once offered Mr. Dishart a snuff from his mull.
In the streets Lang Tammas was more stern and
dreaded by evildoers, but Hendry had first place
in the kirk. One of his duties was to precede
the minister from the session-house to the pulpit
and open the door for him. Having shut Mr.
Dishart in he strolled away to his seat. When
a strange minister preached, Hendry was, if possible, still more at his ease. This will not be
believed, but I have seen him give the pulpit-
door on these occasions a fling-to with his feet.
However ill an ordinary member of the congregation might become in the kirk, he sat on till the
service ended, but Hendry would wander to the
door and shut it if he noticed that the wind was
playing irreverent tricks with the pages of Bibles,
and proof could still be brought forward that he
would stop deliberately in the aisle to lift up a
piece of paper, say, that had floated there. After

the first psalm had been sung it was Hendry's part to lift up the plate and carry its tinkling contents to the session-house. On the greatest occasions he remained so calm, so indifferent, so expressionless, that he might have been present the night before at a rehearsal.

When there was preaching at night the church was lit by tallow candles, which also gave out all the artificial heat provided. Two candles stood on each side of the pulpit, and others were scattered over the church, some of them fixed into holes on rough brackets, and some merely sticking in their own grease on the pews. Hendry superintended the lighting of the candles, and frequently hobbled through the church to snuff them. Mr. Dishart was a man who could do anything except snuff a candle, but when he stopped in his sermon to do that he as often as not knocked the candle over. In vain he sought to refix it in its proper place, and then all eyes turned to Hendry. As coolly as though he were in a public hall or place of entertainment, the kirk-officer arose and, mounting the stair, took the candle from the minister's reluctant hands and put it right. Then he returned to his seat, not apparently puffed up, yet perhaps satisfied with himself; while Mr. Dishart, glaring after him to see if he was carrying his head high, resumed his wordy way.

Never was there a man more uncomfortably

loved than Mr. Dishart. Easie Haggart, his maid-servant, reproved him at the breakfast-table. Lang Tammas and Sam'l Mealmaker crouched for five successive Sabbath nights on his manse wall to catch him smoking (and got him). Old wives grumbled by their hearths when he did not look in to despair of their salvation. He told the maidens of his congregation not to make an idol of him. His session saw him (from behind a hay-stack) in conversation with a strange woman, and asked grimly if he remembered that he had a wife. Twenty were his years when he came to Thrums, and on the very first Sabbath he knocked a board out of the pulpit. Before beginning his trial sermon he handed down the big Bible to the precentor, to give his arms freer swing. The congregation, trembling with exhilaration, probed his meaning. Not a square inch of paper, they saw, could be concealed there. Mr. Dishart had scarcely any hope for the Auld Lichts; he had none for any other denomination. Davit Lunan got behind his handkerchief to think for a moment, and the minister was on him like a tiger. The call was unanimous. Davit proposed him.

Every few years, as one might say, the Auld Licht kirk gave way and buried its minister. The congregation turned their empty pockets inside out, and the minister departed in a farmer's cart. The scene was not an amusing one to those who looked on at it. To the Auld Lichts was then the humiliation of seeing their pulpit "supplied" on alternate Sabbaths by itinerant probationers or stickit ministers. When they were not starving themselves to support a pastor the Auld Lichts were saving up for a stipend. They retired with compressed lips to their looms, and weaved and weaved till they weaved another minister. Without the grief of parting with one minister there could not have been the transport of choosing another. To have had a pastor always might have made them vainglorious.

They were seldom longer than twelve months in making a selection, and in their haste they would have passed over Mr. Dishart and mated with a monster. Many years have elapsed since Providence flung Mr. Watts out of the Auld Licht kirk. Mr. Watts was a probationer who was tried before Mr. Dishart, and, though not so young as might have been wished, he found favour in many eyes. "Sluggard in the laft, awake!" he cried to Bell Whamond, who had forgotten herself, and it was felt that there must be good stuff in him. A breeze from Heaven exposed him on Communion Sabbath.

On the evening of this solemn day the door of the Auld Licht kirk was sometimes locked, and the congregation repaired, Bible in hand, to the commonty. They had a right to this common on the

56

THE AULD LICHT KIRK

Communion Sabbath, but only took advantage of it when it was believed that more persons intended witnessing the evening service than the kirk would hold. On this day the attendance was always very great.

It was the Covenanters come back to life. To the summit of the slope a wooden box was slowly hurled by Hendry Munn and others, and round this the congregation quietly grouped to the tinkle of the cracked Auld Licht bell. With slow majestic tread the session advanced up the steep common with the little minister in their midst. He had the people in his hands now, and the more he squeezed them the better they were pleased. The travelling pulpit consisted of two compartments, the one for the minister and the other for Lang Tammas, but no Auld Licht thought that it looked like a Punch and Judy puppet show. This service on the common was known as the " tent preaching," owing to a tent's being frequently used instead of the box.

Mr. Watts was conducting the service on the commonty. It was a fine, still summer evening, and loud above the whisper of the burn from which the common climbs, and the laboured " pechs " of the listeners rose the preacher's voice. The Auld Lichts in their rusty blacks (they must have been a more artistic sight in the olden days of blue bonnets and knee-breeches) nodded their heads in sharp ap-

57

proval, for though they could swoop down on a
heretic like an eagle on carrion, they scented no
prey. Even Lang Tammas, on whose nose a drop
of water gathered when he was in his greatest fettle,
thought that all was fair and above-board. Suddenly a rush of wind tore up the common, and
ran straight at the pulpit. It formed in a sieve,
and passed over the heads of the congregation, who
felt it as a fan, and looked up in awe. Lang Tammas, feeling himself all at once grow clammy, distinctly heard the leaves of the pulpit Bible shiver.
Mr. Watts's hands, outstretched to prevent a catas-
trophe, were blown against his side, and then some
twenty sheets of closely-written paper floated into
the air. There was a horrible, dead silence. The
burn was roaring now. The minister, if such he
can be called, shrunk back in his box, and, as if
they had seen it printed in letters of fire on the
heavens, the congregation realized that Mr. Watts,
whom they had been on the point of calling, read
his sermon. He wrote it out on pages the exact
size of those in the Bible, and did not scruple to
fasten these into the Holy Book itself. At theatres
a sullen thunder of angry voices behind the scene
represents a crowd in a rage, and such a low, long-
drawn howl swept the common when Mr. Watts
was found out. To follow a pastor who "read"
seemed to the Auld Lichts like claiming heaven on
false pretences. In ten minutes the session alone,

with Lang Tammas and Hendry, were on the common. They were watched by many from afar off, and (when one comes to think of it now) looked a little curious jumping, like trout at flies, at the damning papers still fluttering in the air. The minister was never seen in our parts again, but he is still remembered as " Paper Watts."

Mr. Dishart in the pulpit was the reward of his upbringing. At ten he had entered the university. Before he was in his teens he was practising the art of gesticulation in his father's gallery pew. From distant congregations people came to marvel at him. He was never more than comparatively young. So long as the pulpit trappings of the kirk at Thrums lasted he could be seen, once he was fairly under weigh with his sermon, but dimly in a cloud of dust. He introduced headaches. In a grand transport of enthusiasm he once flung his arms over the pulpit and caught Lang Tammas on the forehead. Leaning forward, with his chest on the cushions, he would pommel the Evil One with both hands, and then, whirling round to the left, shake his fist at Bell Whamond's neckerchief. With a sudden jump he would fix Pete Todd's youngest boy catching flies at the laft window. Stiffening unexpectedly, he would leap three times in the air, and then gather himself in a corner for a fearsome spring. When he wept he seemed to be laughing, and he laughed in a paroxysm of tears.

He tried to tear the devil out of the pulpit rails. When he was not a teetotum he was a windmill. His pump position was the most appalling. Then he glared motionless at his admiring listeners, as if he had fallen into a trance with his arm upraised. The hurricane broke next moment. Nanny Sutie bore up under the shadow of the windmill — which would have been heavier had Auld Licht ministers worn gowns — but the pump affected her to tears. She was stone-deaf.

For the first year or more of his ministry an Auld Licht minister was a mouse among cats. Both in the pulpit and out of it they watched for unsound doctrine, and when he strayed they took him by the neck. Mr. Dishart, however, had been brought up in the true way, and seldom gave his people a chance. In time, it may be said, they grew despondent, and settled in their uncomfortable pews with all suspicion of lurking heresy allayed. It was only on such Sabbaths as Mr. Dishart changed pulpits with another minister that they cocked their ears and leant forward eagerly to snap the preacher up.

Mr. Dishart had his trials. There was the split in the kirk, too, that comes once at least to every Auld Licht minister. He was long in marrying. The congregation were thinking of approaching him, through the medium of his servant, Easie Haggart, on the subject of matrimony; for a bachelor coming on for twenty-two, with an income of eighty pounds per annum, seemed an anomaly, when one day he took the canal for Edinburgh and returned with his bride. His people nodded their heads, but said nothing to the minister. If he did not choose to take them into his confidence, it was no affair of theirs. That there was something queer about the marriage, however, seemed certain. Sandy Whamond, who was a soured man after losing his eldership, said that he believed she had been an "Englishy"—in other words, had belonged to the English Church; but it is not probable that Mr. Dishart would have gone the length of that. The secret is buried in his grave.

Easie Haggart jagged the minister sorely. She grew loquacious with years, and when he had company would stand at the door joining in the conversation. If the company was another minister, she would take a chair and discuss Mr. Dishart's infirmities with him. The Auld Lichts loved their minister, but they saw even more clearly than himself the necessity for his humiliation. His wife made all her children's clothes, but Sanders Gow complained that she looked too like their sister. In one week three of the children died, and on the Sabbath following it rained. Mr. Dishart preached, twice breaking down altogether and gaping strangely round the kirk (there was no dust flying that day), and spoke of the rain as angels' tears for three little girls. The Auld Lichts let it pass, but, as Lang Tammas said in private (for, of course, the thing was much discussed at the looms), if you materialize angels in that way, where are you going to stop?

It was on the Fast Days that the Auld Licht kirk showed what it was capable of, and, so to speak, left all the other churches in Thrums far behind. The Fast came round once every summer, beginning on a Thursday, when all the looms were hushed, and two services were held in the kirk of about three hours' length each. A minister from another town assisted at these times, and when the service ended the members filed in at one door and out at another, passing on their way Mr. Dishart and his elders, who dispensed "tokens" at the foot of the pulpit. Without a token, which was a metal lozenge, no one could take the sacrament on the coming Sabbath, and many a member has Mr. Dishart made miserable by refusing him his token for gathering wild flowers, say, on a Lord's Day (as testified to by another member). Women were lost who cooked dinners on the Sabbath, or took to coloured ribbons, or absented themselves from church without sufficient cause. On the Fast Day fists were shaken at Mr. Dishart as he walked sternly homewards, but he was undismayed. Next day there were no services in the kirk, for Auld Lichts could not afford many holidays, but they weaved solemnly, with Saturday and the Sabbath and Monday to think of. On Saturday service began at two and lasted until nearly seven. Two sermons were preached, but there was no interval. The sacrament was dispensed on the Sabbath. Nowadays the "tables" in the Auld Licht kirk are soon "served," for the attendance has decayed, and most of the pews in the body of the church are made use of. In the days of which I speak, however, the front pews alone were hung with white, and it was in them only that the sacrament was administered. As many members as could get into them delivered up their tokens and took the first table. Then they made room for others, who sat in their pews awaiting their turn. What with tables, the preaching, and unusually long prayers, the service lasted from eleven to six. At half-past six a two hours' service began, either in the kirk or on the common, from which no one who thought much about his immortal soul would have dared (or cared) to absent himself. A four hours' service on the Monday, which, like that of the Saturday, consisted of two services in one, but began at eleven instead of two, completed the programme.

On those days, if you were a poor creature and wanted to acknowledge it, you could leave the church for a few minutes and return to it, but the creditable thing was to sit on. Even among the

children there was a keen competition, fostered by
their parents, to sit each other out, and be in at the
death.

The other Thrums kirks held the sacrament at
the same time, but not with the same vehemence.
As far north from the schoolhouse as Thrums is
south of it, nestles the little village of Quharity,
and there the Fast Day was not a day of fasting.
In most cases the people had to go many miles to
church. They drove or rode (two on a horse), or
walked in from other glens. Without "the tents,"
therefore, the congregation, with a long day before
them, would have been badly off. Sometimes one
tent sufficed; at other times rival publicans were
on the ground. The tents were those in use at the
feeing and other markets, and you could get anything inside them, from broth made in a "boiler"
to the fieriest whisky. They were planted just outside the kirk-gate — long, low tents of dirty white
canvas — so that when passing into the church or
out of it you inhaled their odours. The congregation emerged austerely from the church, shaking
their heads solemnly over the minister's remarks,
and their feet carried them into the tent. There
was no mirth, no unseemly revelry, but there was
a great deal of hard drinking. Eventually the
tents were done away with, but not until the services on the Fast Days were shortened. The Auld
Licht ministers were the only ones who preached

against the tents with any heart, and since the old dominie, my predecessor at the schoolhouse, died, there has not been an Auld Licht permanently resident in the glen of Quharity.

Perhaps nothing took it out of the Auld Licht males so much as a christening. Then alone they showed symptoms of nervousness, more especially after the remarkable baptism of Eppie Whamond. I could tell of several scandals in connection with the kirk. There was, for instance, the time when Easie Haggart saved the minister. In a fit of temporary mental derangement the misguided man had one Sabbath day, despite the entreaties of his affrighted spouse, called at the post-office, and was on the point of reading the letter there received, when Easie, who had slipped on her bonnet and followed him, snatched the secular thing from his hands. There was the story that ran like fire through Thrums and crushed an innocent man to the effect that Pete Todd had been in an Edinburgh theatre countenancing the play-actors. Something could be made, too, of the retribution that came to Chairlie Ramsay, who woke in his pew to discover that its other occupant, his little son Jamie, was standing on the seat divesting himself of his clothes in presence of a horrified congregation. Jamie had begun stealthily, and had very little on when Chairlie seized him. But having my choice of scandals I prefer the christening one — the unique case of Eppie Whamond, who was born late on Saturday night and baptized in the kirk on the following forenoon.

To the casual observer the Auld Licht always looked as if he were returning from burying a near relative. Yet when I met him hobbling down the street, preternaturally grave and occupied, experience taught me that he was preparing for a christening. How the minister would have borne himself in the event of a member of his congregation's wanting the baptism to take place at home it is not easy to say; but I shudder to think of the public prayers for the parents that would certainly have followed. The child was carried to the kirk through rain, or snow, or sleet, or wind, the father took his seat alone in the front pew, under the minister's eye, and the service was prolonged far on into the afternoon. But though the references in the sermon to that unhappy object of interest in the front pew were many and pointed, his time had not really come until the minister signed to him to advance as far as the second step of the pulpit stairs. The nervous father clenched the railing in a daze, and cowered before the ministerial heckling. From warning the minister passed to exhortation, from exhortation to admonition, from admonition to searching questioning, from questioning to prayer and wailing. When the father glanced up, there was the radiant boy in the pulpit looking as if he would like to jump down his throat. If he hung his head the minister would ask, with a groan, whether he was unprepared; and the whole congregation would sigh out the response that Mr. Dishard had hit it. When he replied audibly to the minister's uncomfortable questions, a pained look at his flippancy travelled from the pulpit all round the pews; and when he only bowed his head in answer, the minister paused sternly, and the congregation wondered what the man meant. Little wonder that Davie Haggart took to drinking when his turn came for occupying that front pew.

If wee Eppie Whamond's birth had been deferred until the beginning of the week, or humility had shown more prominently among her mother's virtues, the kirk would have been saved a painful scandal, and Sandy Whamond might have retained his eldership. Yet it was a foolish but wifely pride in her husband's official position that turned Bell Dundas's head — a wild ambition to beat all baptismal record.

Among the wives she was esteemed a poor body whose infant did not see the inside of the kirk within a fortnight of its birth. Forty years ago it was an accepted superstition in Thrums that the ghosts of children who had died before they were baptized went wailing and wringing their hands round the kirkyard at nights, and that they would continue to do this until the crack of doom. When the Auld Licht children grew up, too, they crowed over those of their fellows whose christening had been deferred until a comparatively late date, and the mothers who had needlessly missed a Sabbath for long afterwards hung their heads. That was a good and creditable birth which took place early in the week, thus allowing time for suitable christening preparations; while to be born on a Friday or a Saturday was to humiliate your parents, besides being an extremely ominous beginning for yourself. Without seeking to vindicate Bell Dundas's behaviour, I may note, as an act of ordinary fairness, that being the leading elder's wife, she was sorely tempted. Eppie made her appearance at 9.45 on a Saturday night.

In the hurry and scurry that ensued, Sandy escaped sadly to the square. His infant would be baptized eight days old, one of the longest-deferred christenings of the year. Sandy was shivering under the clock when I met him accidentally, and took him home. But by that time the harm had been done. Several of the congregation had been roused from their beds to hear his lamentations, of whom the men sympathized with him, while the wives triumphed austerely over Bell Dundas. As I wrung poor Sandy's hand, I hardly noticed that a bright light showed distinctly between the shutters of his kitchen-window; but the elder himself turned pale and breathed quickly. It was then fourteen minutes past twelve.

My heart sank within me on the following forenoon, when Sandy Whamond walked, with a queer twitching face, into the front pew under a glare of eyes from the body of the kirk and the laft. An amazed buzz went round the church, followed by a pursing up of lips and hurried whisperings. Evidently Sandy had been driven to it against his own judgment. The scene is still vivid before me: the minister suspecting no guile, and omitting the admonitory stage out of compliment to the elder's standing; Sandy's ghastly face; the proud godmother (aged twelve) with the squalling baby in her arms; the horror of the congregation to a man and woman. A slate fell from Sandy's house even as he held up the babe to the minister to receive a "droukin'" of water, and Eppie cried so vigorously that her shamed godmother had to rush with her to the vestry. Now things are not as they should be when an Auld Licht infant does not quietly sit out her first service.

Bell tried for a time to carry her head high; but Sandy ceased to whistle at his loom, and the scandal was a rolling stone that soon passed over him. Briefly it amounted to this: that a bairn born within two hours of midnight on Saturday could not have been ready for christening at the kirk next day without the breaking of the Sabbath. Had the secret of the nocturnal light been mine alone all might have been well; but Betsy Munn's evidence was irrefutable. Great had been Bell's cunning, but Betsy had outwitted her. Passing the house on the eventful night, Betsy had observed Marget Dundas, Bell's sister, open the door and creep cautiously to the window, the chinks in the outside shutters of which she cunningly closed up with " tow." As in a flash the disgusted Betsy saw what Bell was up to, and, removing the tow, planted herself behind the dilapidated dyke opposite, and awaited events. Questioned at a special meeting of the office-bearers in the vestry, she admitted that the lamp was extinguished soon after twelve o'clock, though the fire burned brightly all night. There had been unnecessary feasting during the night, and six eggs were consumed before breakfast-time. Asked how she knew this, she admitted having counted the egg-shells that Marget had thrown out of doors in the morning. This, with the testimony of the persons from whom Sandy had sought condolence on the Saturday night, was the case for the prosecution. For the defence, Bell maintained that all preparations stopped when the clock struck twelve, and even hinted that the bairn had been born on Saturday afternoon. But Sandy knew that he and his had got a fall. In the forenoon of the follow-

ing Sabbath the minister preached from the text,
" Be sure your sin will find you out ; " and in the
afternoon from " Pride goeth before a fall." He
was grand. In the evening Sandy tendered his re-
signation of office, which was at once accepted.
Wobs were behindhand for a week owing to the
length of the prayers offered up for Bell; and
Lang Tammas ruled in Sandy's stead.

CHAPTER IV

LADS AND LASSES

WITH the severe Auld Lichts the Sabbath began at six o'clock on Saturday evening. By that time the gleaming shuttle was at rest, Davie Haggart had strolled into the village from his pile of stones on the Whunny road; Hendry Robb, the "dummy," had sold his last barrowful of "rozetty (resiny) roots" for firewood; and the people, having tranquilly supped and soused their faces in their water-pails, slowly donned their Sunday clothes. This ceremony was common to all; but here divergence set in. The grey Auld Licht, to whom love was not even a name, sat in his high-backed arm-chair by the hearth, Bible or "Pilgrim's Progress" in hand, occasionally lapsing into slumber. But—though, when they got the chance, they went willingly three times to the kirk—there were young men in the community so flighty that, instead of dozing at home on Saturday night, they dandered casually into the square, and, forming into knots at the corners, talked solemnly and mysteriously of women.

Not even on the night preceding his wedding

72

was an Auld Licht ever known to stay out after ten o'clock. So weekly conclaves at street-corners came to an end at a comparatively early hour, one Cœlebs after another shuffling silently from the square until it echoed, deserted, to the town-house clock. The last of the gallants, gradually discovering that he was alone, would look around him musingly, and, taking in the situation, slowly wend his way home. On no other night of the week was frivolous talk about the softer sex indulged in, the Auld Lichts being creatures of habit who never thought of smiling on a Monday. Long before they reached their teens they were earning their keep as herds in the surrounding glens or filling " pirns " for their parents; but they were generally on the brink of twenty before they thought seriously of matrimony. Up to that time they only trifled with the other sex's affections at a distance — filling a maid's water-pails, perhaps, when no one was looking, or carrying her wob; at the recollection of which they would slap their knees almost jovially on Saturday night. A wife was expected to assist at the loom as well as to be cunning in the making of marmalade and the firing of bannocks, and there was consequently some heartburning among the lads for maids of skill and muscle. The Auld Licht, however, who meant marriage seldom loitered in the streets. By and by there came a time when the clock

looked down through its cracked glass upon the
hemmed in square and saw him not. His companions, gazing at each other's boots, felt that something was going on, but made no remark.

A month ago, passing through the shabby familiar square, I brushed against a withered old man
tottering down the street under a load of yarn. It
was piled on a wheelbarrow which his feeble hands
could not have raised but for the rope of yarn that
supported it from his shoulders; and though Auld
Licht was written on his patient eyes, I did not
immediately recognize Jamie Whamond. Years
ago Jamie was a sturdy weaver and fervent lover
whom I had the right to call my friend. Turn back
the century a few decades, and we are together on a
moonlight night, taking a short cut through the
fields from the farm of Craigiebuckle. Buxom
were Craigiebuckle's " dochters," and Jamie was
Janet's accepted suitor. It was a muddy road
through damp grass, and we picked our way silently
over its ruts and pools. " I'm thinkin'," Jamie
said at last, a little wistfully, " that I micht hae
been as weel wi' Chirsty." Chirsty was Janet's
sister, and Jamie had first thought of her. Craigiebuckle, however, strongly advised him to take
Janet instead, and he consented. Alack! heavy
wobs have taken all the grace from Janet's shoulders this many a year, though she and Jamie go
bravely down the hill together. Unless they pass

the allotted span of life, the "poorshouse" will
never know them. As for bonny Chirsty, she
proved a flighty thing, and married a deacon in the
Established Church. The Auld Lichts groaned
over her fall, Craigiebuckle hung his head, and
the minister told her sternly to go her way. But
a few weeks afterwards Lang Tammas, the chief
elder, was observed talking with her for an hour
in Gowrie's close; and the very next Sabbath
Chirsty pushed her husband in triumph into her
father's pew. The minister, though completely
taken by surprise, at once referred to the stranger,
in a prayer of great length, as a brand that might
yet be plucked from the burning. Changing his
text, he preached at him; Lang Tammas, the precentor, and the whole congregation (Chirsty included), sang at him; and before he exactly realized
his position he had become an Auld Licht for life.
Chirsty's triumph was complete when, next week,
in broad daylight, too, the minister's wife called,
and (in the presence of Betsy Munn, who vouches
for the truth of the story) graciously asked her to
come up to the manse on Thursday, at 4 p. m.,
and drink a dish of tea. Chirsty, who knew her
position, of course begged modestly to be excused;
but a coolness arose over the invitation between
her and Janet — who felt slighted — that was only
made up at the laying-out of Chirsty's father-in-
law, to which Janet was pleasantly invited.

When they had red up the house, the Auld
Licht lassies sat in the gloaming at their doors on
three-legged stools, patiently knitting stockings.
To them came stiff-limbed youths who, with a
" Blawy nicht, Jeanie " (to which the inevitable
answer was, " It is so, Cha-rles "), rested their
shoulders on the doorpost, and silently followed
with their eyes the flashing needles. Thus the
courtship began — often to ripen promptly into
marriage, at other times to go no further. The
smooth-haired maids, neat in their simple wrap-
pers, knew they were on their trial and that it
behoved them to be wary. They had not com-
passed twenty winters without knowing that Marget Todd lost Davie Haggart because she " fittit "
a black stocking with brown worsted, and that
Finny's grieve turned from Bell Whamond on account of the frivolous flowers in her bonnet : and
yet Bell's prospects, as I happen to know, at one
time looked bright and promising. Sitting over
her father's peat-fire one night gossiping with him
about fishing-flies and tackle, I noticed the grieve,
who had dropped in by appointment with some
ducks' eggs on which Bell's clockin hen was to
sit, performing some sleight-of-hand trick with his
coat-sleeve. Craftily he jerked and twisted it, till
his own photograph (a black smudge on white)
gradually appeared to view. This he gravely
slipped into the hands of the maid of his choice,

and then took his departure, apparently much relieved. Had not Bell's light-headedness driven him away, the grieve would have soon followed up his gift with an offer of his hand. Some night Bell would have "seen him to the door," and they would have stared sheepishly at each other before saying good-night. The parting salutation given, the grieve would still have stood his ground, and Bell would have waited with him. At last, "Will ye hae's, Bell?" would have dropped from his half-reluctant lips; and Bell would have mumbled "Ay," with her thumb in her mouth. "Guid nicht to ye, Bell," would be the next remark — "Guid nicht to ye, Jeames," the answer; the humble door would close softly, and Bell and her lad would have been engaged. But, as it was, their attachment never got beyond the silhouette stage, from which, in the ethics of the Auld Lichts, a man can draw back in certain circumstances, without loss of honour. The only really tender thing I ever heard an Auld Licht lover say to his sweetheart was when Gowrie's brother looked softly into Easie Tamson's eyes and whispered, "Do you swite (sweat)?" Even then the effect was produced more by the loving cast in Gowrie's eye than by the tenderness of the words themselves.

The courtships were sometimes of long duration, but as soon as the young man realized that he was courting he proposed. Cases were not

wanting in which he realized this for himself, but
as a rule he had to be told of it.

There were a few instances of weddings among
the Auld Lichts that did not take place on Friday.
Betsy Munn's brother thought to assert his two
coal-carts, about which he was sinfully puffed up,
by getting married early in the week; but he was
a pragmatical feckless body, Jamie. The foreigner
from York that Finny's grieve after disappoint-
ing Bell Whamond took, sought to sow the seeds
of strife by urging that Friday was an unlucky
day; and I remember how the minister, who was
always great in a crisis, nipped the bickering in
the bud by adducing the conclusive fact that he
had been married on the sixth day of the week
himself. It was a judicious policy on Mr. Dishart's part to take vigorous action at once and in-
sist on the solemnization of the marriage on a
Friday or not at all, for he best kept superstition
out of the congregation by branding it as heresy.
Perhaps the Auld Lichts were only ignorant of
the grieve's lass's theory because they had not
thought of it. Friday's claims, too, were incon-
trovertible; for the Saturday's being a slack day
gave the couple an opportunity to put their but
and ben in order, and on Sabbath they had a gay
day of it, three times at the kirk. The honeymoon
over, the racket of the loom began again on the
Monday.

The natural politeness of the Allardice family gave me my invitation to Tibbie's wedding. I was taking tea and cheese early one wintry afternoon with the smith and his wife, when little Joey Todd in his Sabbath clothes peered in at the passage, and then knocked primly at the door. Andra forgot himself, and called out to him to come in by; but Jess frowned him into silence, and hastily donning her black mutch, received Willie on the threshold. Both halves of the door were open, and the visitor had looked us over carefully before knocking; but he had come with the compliments of Tibbie's mother, requesting the pleasure of Jess and her man that evening to the lassie's marriage with Sam'l Todd, and the knocking at the door was part of the ceremony. Five minutes afterwards Joey returned to beg a moment of me in the passage; when I, too, got my invitation. The lad had just received, with an expression of polite surprise, though he knew he could claim it as his right, a slice of crumbling shortbread, and taken his staid departure, when Jess cleared the teathings off the table, remarking simply that it was a mercy we had not got beyond the first cup. We then retired to dress.

About six o'clock, the time announced for the ceremony, I elbowed my way through the expectant throng of men, women, and children that already besieged the smith's door. Shrill demands

79

of "Toss, toss!" rent the air every time Jess's head showed on the window-blind, and Andra hoped, as I pushed open the door, "that I hadna forgotten my bawbees." Weddings were celebrated among the Auld Lichts by showers of ha'-pence, and the guests on their way to the bride's house had to scatter to the hungry rabble like housewives feeding poultry. Willie Todd, the best man, who had never come out so strong in his life before, slipped through the back window, while the crowd, led on by Kitty McQueen, seethed in front, and making a bolt for it to the "'Sosh," was back in a moment with a handful of small change. "Dinna toss ower lavishly at first," the smith whispered me nervously, as we followed Jess and Willie into the darkening wynd.

The guests were packed hot and solemn in Johnny Allardice's "room:" the men anxious to surrender their seats to the ladies who happened to be standing, but too bashful to propose it; the ham and the fish frizzling noisily side by side but the house, and hissing out every now and then to let all whom it might concern know that Janet Craik was adding more water to the gravy. A better woman never lived; but, oh, the hypocrisy of the face that beamed greeting to the guests as if it had nothing to do but politely show them in, and gasped next moment with upraised arms, over what was nearly a fall in crockery. When Janet

sped to the door her "spleet new" merino dress
fell, to the pulling of a string, over her home-made
petticoat, like the drop-scene in a theatre, and rose
as promptly when she returned to slice the bacon.
The murmur of admiration that filled the room
when she entered with the minister was an involuntary tribute to the spotlessness of her wrapper
and a great triumph for Janet. If there is an impression that the dress of the Auld Lichts was on
all occasions as sombre as their faces, let it be
known that the bride was but one of several in
"whites," and that Mag Munn had only at the
last moment been dissuaded from wearing flowers.
The minister, the Auld Lichts congratulated themselves, disapproved of all such decking of the person and bowing of the head to idols; but on such
an occasion he was not expected to observe it.
Bell Whamond, however, has reason for knowing
that, marriages or no marriages, he drew the line
at curls.

By and by Sam'l Todd, looking a little dazed,
was pushed into the middle of the room to Tibbie's side, and the minister raised his voice in
prayer. All eyes closed reverently, except perhaps the bridegroom's, which seemed glazed and
vacant. It was an open question in the community whether Mr. Dishart did not miss his chance at
weddings; the men shaking their heads over the
comparative brevity of the ceremony, the women

worshipping him (though he never hesitated to rebuke them when they showed it too openly) for the urbanity of his manners. At that time, however, only a minister of such experience as Mr. Dishart's predecessor could lead up to a marriage in prayer without inadvertently joining the couple; and the catechizing was mercifully brief. Another prayer followed the union; the minister waived his right to kiss the bride; every one looked at every other one, as if he had for the moment forgotten what he was on the point of saying and found it very annoying; and Janet signed frantically to Willie Todd, who nodded intelligently in reply, but evidently had no idea what she meant. In time Johnny Allardice, our host, who became more and more doited as the night proceeded, remembered his instructions, and led the way to the kitchen, where the guests, having politely informed their hostess that they were not hungry, partook of a hearty tea. Mr. Dishart presided with the bride and bridegroom near him; but though he tried to give an agreeable turn to the conversation by describing the extensions at the cemetery, his personality oppressed us, and we only breathed freely when he rose to go. Yet we marvelled at his versatility. In shaking hands with the newly-married couple the minister reminded them that it was leap-year, and wished them "three hundred and sixty-six happy and God-fearing days."

LADS AND LASSES

Sam'l's station being too high for it, Tibbie did
not have a penny wedding, which her thrifty mother bewailed, penny weddings starting a couple in
life. I can recall nothing more characteristic of
the nation from which the Auld Lichts sprung
than the penny wedding, where the only revellers
that were not out of pocket by it, were the couple
who gave the entertainment. The more the guests
ate and drank the better, pecuniarily, for their
hosts. The charge for admission to the penny
wedding (practically to the feast that followed it)
varied in different districts, but with us it was
generally a shilling. Perhaps the penny extra to
the fiddler accounts for the name penny wedding.
The ceremony having been gone through in the
bride's house, there was an adjournment to a barn
or other convenient place of meeting, where was
held the nuptial feast; long white boards from Rob
Angus's sawmill, supported on trestles, stood in
lieu of tables; and those of the company who
could not find a seat waited patiently against the
wall for a vacancy. The shilling gave every guest
the free run of the groaning board, but though
fowls were plentiful, and even white bread too,
little had been spent on them. The farmers of
the neighbourhood, who looked forward to providing the young people with drills of potatoes
for the coming winter, made a bid for their custom by sending them a fowl gratis for the mar-

83

riage supper. It was popularly understood to be the oldest cock of the farmyard, but for all that it made a brave appearance in a shallow sea of soup. The fowls were always boiled — without exception, so far as my memory carries me; the guidwife never having the heart to roast them, and so lose the broth. One round of whisky-and-water was all the drink to which his shilling entitled the guest. If he wanted more he had to pay for it. There was much revelry, with song and dance, that no stranger could have thought those stifflimbed weavers capable of; and the more they shouted and whirled through the barn, the more their host smiled and rubbed his hands. He presided at the bar improvised for the occasion, and if the thing was conducted with spirit, his bride flung an apron over her gown and helped him. I remember one elderly bridegroom, who, having married a blind woman, had to do double work at his penny wedding. It was a sight to see him flitting about the torch-lit barn, with a kettle of hot water in one hand and a besom to sweep up crumbs in the other.

Though Sam'l had no penny wedding, however, we made a night of it at his marriage.

Wedding chariots were not in those days, though I know of Auld Lichts being conveyed to marriages nowadays by horses with white ears. The tea over, we formed in couples, and — the

84

best man with the bride, the bridegroom with the best maid, leading the way — marched in slow procession in the moonlight night to Tibbie's new home, between lines of hoarse and eager onlookers. An attempt was made by an itinerant musician to head the company with his fiddle; but instrumental music, even in the streets, was abhorrent to sound Auld Lichts, and the minister had spoken privately to Willie Todd on the subject. As a consequence, Peter was driven from the ranks. The last thing I saw that night, as we filed, bare-headed and solemn, into the newly-married couple's house, was Kitty McQueen's vigorous arm, in a dishevelled sleeve, pounding a pair of urchins who had got between her and a muddy ha'penny.

That night there was revelry and boisterous mirth (or what the Auld Lichts took for such) in Tibbie's kitchen. At eleven o'clock Davit Lunan cracked a joke. Davie Haggart, in reply to Bell Dundas's request, gave a song of distinctly secular tendencies. The bride (who had carefully taken off her wedding gown on getting home and donned a wrapper) coquettishly let the bridegroom's father hold her hand. In Auld Licht circles, when one of the company was offered whisky and refused it, the others, as if pained even at the offer, pushed it from them as a thing abhorred. But Davie Haggart set another example on this occasion, and no one had the courage to refuse to follow it. We sat late round the dying fire, and it was only Willie Todd's scandalous assertion (he was but a boy) about his being able to dance that induced us to think of moving. In the community, I understand, this marriage is still memorable as the occasion on which Bell Whamond laughed in the minister's face.

CHAPTER V

THE AULD LICHTS IN ARMS

ARMS and men I sing: douce Jeemsy Todd, rushing from his loom, armed with a bed-post; Lisbeth Whamond, an avenging whirlwind; Neil Haggart, pausing in his thanks-offerings to smite and slay; the impious foe scudding up the bleeding Brae-head with Nemesis at their flashing heels; the minister holding it a nice question whether the carnage was not justified. Then came the two hours' sermons of the following Sabbath, when Mr. Dishart, revolving like a teetotum in the pulpit, damned every bandaged person present, individually and collectively; and Lang Tammas, in the precentor's box with a plaster on his cheek, included any one the minister might have by chance omitted, and the congregation, with most of their eyes bunged up, burst into psalms of praise.

Twice a year the Auld Lichts went demented. The occasion was the Fast Day at Tilliedrum; when its inhabitants, instead of crowding reverently to the kirk, swooped profanely down in their scores and tens of scores on our God-fearing town, intent

87

on making a day of it. Then did the weavers rise
as one man, and go forth to show the ribald crew
the errors of their way. All denominations were
represented, but Auld Lichts led. An Auld Licht
would have taken no man's blood without the
conviction that he would be the better morally for
the bleeding; and if Tammas Lunan's case gave
an impetus to the blows, it can only have been
because it opened wider Auld Licht eyes to Tilliedrum's desperate condition. Mr. Dishart's predecessor more than once remarked, that at the
Creation the devil put forward a claim for Thrums,
but said he would take his chance of Tilliedrum;
and the statement was generally understood to be
made on the authority of the original Hebrew.

The mustard-seed of a feud between the two
parishes shot into a tall tree in a single night, when
Davit Lunan's father went to a tattie roup at
Tilliedrum and thoughtlessly died there. Twenty-
four hours afterwards a small party of staid Auld
Lichts, carrying long white poles, stepped out of
various wynds and closes and picked their solemn
way to the house of mourning. Nanny Low, the
widow, received them dejectedly, as one oppressed
by the knowledge that her man's death at such an
inopportune place did not fulfil the promise of his
youth; and her guests admitted bluntly that they
were disappointed in Tammas. Snecky Hobart's
father's unusually long and impressive prayer was

an official intimation that the deceased, in the opinion of the session, sorely needed everything of the kind he could get; and then the silent driblet of Auld Lichts in black stalked off in the direction of Tilliedrum. Women left their spinning-wheels and pirns to follow them with their eyes along the Tenements, and the minister was known to be holding an extra service at the manse. When the little procession reached the boundary-line between the two parishes, they sat down on a dyke and waited.

By and by half a dozen men drew near from the opposite direction, bearing on poles the remains of Tammas Lunan in a closed coffin. The coffin was brought to within thirty yards of those who awaited it, and then roughly lowered to the ground. Its bearers rested morosely on their poles. In conveying Lunan's remains to the borders of his own parish they were only conforming to custom; but Thrums and Tilliedrum differed as to where the boundary-line was drawn, and not a foot would either advance into the other's territory. For half a day the coffin lay unclaimed, and the two parties sat scowling at each other. Neither dared move. Gloaming had stolen into the valley when Dite Deuchars of Tilliedrum rose to his feet and deliberately spat upon the coffin. A stone whizzed through the air; and then the ugly spectacle was presented, in the grey night, of a dozen mutes fighting with their poles over a coffin. There was blood on the shoulders that bore Tammas's remains to Thrums.

After that meeting Tilliedrum lived for the Fast Day. Never, perhaps, was there a community more given up to sin, and Thrums felt "called" to its chastisement. The insult to Lunan's coffin, however, dispirited their weavers for a time, and not until the suicide of Pitlums did they put much fervour into their prayers. It made new men of them. Tilliedrum's sins had found it out. Pitlums was a farmer in the parish of Thrums, but he had been born at Tilliedrum; and Thrums thanked Providence for that, when it saw him suspended between two hams from his kitchen rafters. The custom was to cart suicides to the quarry at the Galla pond and bury them near the cairn that had supported the gallows; but on this occasion not a farmer in the parish would lend a cart, and for a week the corpse lay on the sanded floor as it had been cut down — an object of awe-struck interest to boys who knew no better than to peep through the darkened window. Tilliedrum bit its lips at home. The Auld Licht minister, it was said, had been approached on the subject; but, after serious consideration, did not see his way to offering up a prayer. Finally old Hobart and two others tied a rope round the body, and dragged it from the farm to the cairn, a distance of four miles.

THE AULD LICHTS IN ARMS

Instead of this incident's humbling Tilliedrum into attending church, the next Fast Day saw its streets deserted. As for the Thrums Auld Lichts, only heavy wobs prevented their walking erect like men who had done their duty. If no prayer was volunteered for Pitlums before his burial, there was a great deal of psalm-singing after it.

By early morn on their Fast Day the Tillie-drummers were straggling into Thrums, and the weavers, already at their looms, read the clattering of feet and carts aright. To convince themselves, all they had to do was to raise their eyes; but the first triumph would have been to Tilliedrum if they had done that. The invaders — the men in Aberdeen blue serge coats, velvet knee-breeches, and broad blue bonnets, and the wincey gowns of the women set off with hooded cloaks of red or tartan — tapped at the windows and shouted insultingly as they passed; but, with pursed lips, Thrums bent fiercely over its wobs, and not an Auld Licht showed outside his door. The day wore on to noon, and still ribaldry was master of the wynds. But there was a change inside the houses. The minister had pulled down his blinds; moody men had left their looms for stools by the fire; there were rumours of a conflict in Andra Gowrie's close, from which Kitty McQueen had emerged with her short gown in rags; and Lang Tammas was going from door to door. The austere precentor admonished fiery youth to beware of giving way to passion; and it was a proud day for the Auld Lichts to find their leading elder so conversant with apt Scripture texts. They bowed their heads reverently while he thundered forth that those who lived by the sword would perish by the sword; and when he had finished they took him ben to inspect their bludgeons. I have a vivid recollection of going the round of the Auld Licht and other houses to see the sticks and the wrists in coils of wire.

A stranger in the Tenements in the afternoon would have noted more than one draggled youth, in holiday attire, sitting on a doorstep with a wet cloth to his nose; and, passing down the Commonty, he would have had to step over prostrate lumps of humanity from which all shape had departed. Gavin Ogilvy limped heavily after his encounter with Thrummy Tosh — a struggle that was looked forward to eagerly as a bi-yearly event; Chirsty Davie's development of muscle had not prevented her going down before the terrible onslaught of Joe the miller, and Lang Tammas's plasters told a tale. It was in the square that the two parties, leading their maimed and blind, formed in force; Tilliedrum thirsting for its opponents' blood, and Thrums humbly accepting the responsibility of punching the Fast Day breakers into the ways of rectitude. In the small ill-kept square the invaders, to the number of about a hundred, were wedged together at its upper end, while the Thrums people formed in a thick line at the foot. For its inhabitants the way to Tilliedrum lay through this threatening mass of armed weavers. No words were bandied between the two forces; the centre of the square was left open, and nearly every eye was fixed on the town-house clock. It directed operations and gave the signal to charge. The moment six o'clock struck, the upper mass broke its bonds and flung itself on the living barricade. There was a clatter of heads and sticks, a yelling and a groaning, and then the invaders, bursting through the opposing ranks, fled for Tilliedrum. Down the Tanage brae and up the Braehead they skurried, half a hundred avenging spirits in pursuit. On the Tilliedrum Fast Day I have tasted blood myself. In the godless place there is no Auld Licht kirk, but there are two Auld Lichts in it now who walk to Thrums to church every Sabbath, blow or rain as it lists. They are making their influence felt in Tilliedrum.

The Auld Lichts also did valorous deeds at the Battle of Cabbylatch. The farm land so named lies a mile or more to the south of Thrums. You have to go over the rim of the cup to reach it. It is low-lying and uninteresting to the eye, except for some giant stones scattered cold and naked through the fields. No human hands reared these boulders, but they might be looked upon as tomb-stones to the heroes who fell (to rise hurriedly) on the plain of Cabbylatch.

The fight of Cabbylatch belongs to the days of what are now but dimly remembered as the Meal Mobs. Then there was a wild cry all over the country for bread (not the fine loaves that we know, but something very much coarser), and hungry men and women, prematurely shrunken, began to forget the taste of meal. Potatoes were their chief sustenance, and, when the crop failed, starvation gripped them. At that time the far-mers, having control of the meal, had the small towns at their mercy, and they increased its cost. The price of the meal went up and up, until the famishing people swarmed up the sides of the carts in which it was conveyed to the towns, and, tearing open the sacks, devoured it in handfuls. In Thrums they had a stern sense of justice, and for a time, after taking possession of the meal, they carried it to the square and sold it at what they considered a reasonable price. The money was handed over to the farmers. The honesty of this is worth thinking about, but it seems to have only incensed the farmers the more; and when they saw that to send their meal to the town was not to get high prices for it, they laid their heads together and then gave notice that the people who wanted meal and were able to pay for it must come to the farms. In Thrums no one who cared to live on porridge and bannocks had money to satisfy the farmers; but, on the other hand, none of them grudged going for it, and go they did. They went in numbers from farm to farm, like bands of hungry rats, and throttled the opposition they not infrequently encountered. The raging farmers at last met in council and, noting that they were lusty men and brave, resolved to march in armed force upon the erring people and burn their town. Now we come to the Battle of Cabbylatch.

The farmers were not less than eighty strong, and chiefly consisted of cavalry. Armed with pitchforks and cumbrous scythes where they were not able to lay their hands on the more orthodox weapons of war, they presented a determined appearance; the few foot-soldiers who had no carthorses at their disposal bearing in their arms bundles of fire-wood. One memorable morning they set out to avenge their losses; and by and by a halt was called, when each man bowed his head to listen. In Thrums, pipe and drum were calling the inhabitants to arms. Scouts rushed in with the news that the farmers were advancing rapidly upon the town, and soon the streets were clattering with feet. At that time Thrums had its piper and drummer (the bellman of a later and more degenerate age); and on this occasion they marched together through the narrow wynds, firing the blood of haggard men and summoning them to the square. According to my informant's father, the gathering of these angry and startled weavers, when he thrust his blue bonnet on his head and rushed out to join them, was an impressive and solemn spectacle. That bloodshed was meant there can be no doubt; for starving men do not see the ludicrous side of things. The difference between the farmers and the town had resolved itself into an ugly and sullen hate, and the wealthier townsmen who would have come between the people and the bread were fiercely pushed aside. There was no nominal leader, but every man in the ranks meant to fight for himself and his belongings; and they are said to have sallied out to meet the foe in no disorder. The women they would fain have left behind them; but these had their own injuries to redress, and they followed in their husbands' wake carrying bags of stones. The men, who were of various denominations, were armed with sticks, blunderbusses, anything they could snatch up at a moment's notice; and some of them were not unacquainted with fighting. Dire silence prevailed among the men, but the women shouted as they ran, and the curious army moved forward to the drone and squall of drum and pipe. The enemy was sighted on the level land of Cabbylatch; and here, while the intending combatants glared at each other, a well-known local magnate galloped his horse between them and ordered them in the name of the King to return to their homes. But for the farmers that meant further depredation at the people's hands, and the townsmen would not go back to their gloomy homes to sit down and wait for sunshine. Soon stones (the first, it is said, cast by a woman) darkened the air. The farmers got the word to charge, but their horses, with the best intentions, did not know the way. There was a stampeding in different directions, a blind rushing of one frightened steed against another; and then the townspeople, breaking any ranks they had hitherto managed to keep, rushed vindictively forward. The struggle at Cabbylatch itself was not of long duration; for their own horses proved the farmers' worst enemies, except in the cases where these sagacious animals took matters into their own ordering and bolted judiciously for their stables. The day was to Thrums.

Individual deeds of prowess were done that day. Of these not the least fondly remembered by her descendants were those of the gallant matron who pursued the most obnoxious farmer in the district even to his very porch with heavy stones and opprobrious epithets. Once when he thought he had left her far behind did he alight to draw breath and take a pinch of snuff, and she was upon him like a flail. With a terror-stricken cry he leapt once more upon his horse and fled, but not without leaving his snuff-box in the hands of the derisive enemy. Meggy has long gone to the kirk-yard, but the snuff-mull is still preserved.

Some ugly cuts were given and received, and heads as well as ribs were broken; but the townsmen's triumph was short-lived. The ringleaders were whipped through the streets of Perth, as a warning to persons thinking of taking the law into their own hands; and all the lasting consolation they got was that, some time afterwards, the chief witness against them, the parish minister, met with a mysterious death. They said it was evidently the hand of God; but some people looked suspiciously at them when they said it.

CHAPTER VI

THE OLD DOMINIE

FROM the new cemetery, which is the highest point in Thrums, you just fail to catch sight of the red schoolhouse that nestles between two bare trees, some five miles up the glen of Quharity. This was proved by Davit Lunan, tinsmith, whom I have heard tell the story. It was in the time when the cemetery gates were locked to keep the bodies of suicides out, but men who cared to risk the consequences could get the coffin over the high dyke and bury it themselves. Peter Lundy's coffin broke, as one might say, into the churchyard in this way, Peter having hanged himself in the Whunny wood when he saw that work he must. The general feeling among the intimates of the deceased was expressed by Davit when he said:

" It may do the crittur nae guid i' the tail o' the day, but he paid for's bit o' ground, an' he's in's richt to occupy it."

The custom was to push the coffin on to the wall up a plank, and then let it drop less carefully into the cemetery. Some of the mourners were drag-

ging the plank over the wall, with Davit Lunan on
the top directing them, when they seem to have
let go and sent the tinsmith suddenly into the air.
A week afterwards it struck Davit, when in the
act of soldering a hole in Leeby Wheens's flagon
(here he branched off to explain that he had made
the flagon years before, and that Leeby was sister
to Tammas Wheens, and married one Baker Robbie, who died of chicken-pox in his forty-fourth
year), that when "up there" he had a view of
Quharity schoolhouse. Davit was as truthful as
a man who tells the same story more than once
can be expected to be, and it is far from a suspicious circumstance that he did not remember
seeing the schoolhouse all at once. In Thrums
things only struck them gradually. The new
cemetery, for instance, was only so called because
it had been new once.

In this red stone school, full of the modern im-
provements that he detested, the old dominie whom
I succeeded taught, and sometimes slept, during
the last five years of his cantankerous life. It was
in a little thatched school, consisting of but one
room, that he did his best work, some five hundred yards away from the edifice that was reared
in its stead. Now dismally fallen into disrepute,
often indeed a domicile for cattle, the ragged acad-
emy of Glen Quharity, where he held despotic
sway for nearly half a century, is falling to pieces

slowly in a howe that conceals it from the high road. Even in its best scholastic days, when it sent barefooted lads to college who helped to hasten the Disruption, it was but a pile of ungainly stones, such as Scott's Black Dwarf flung together in a night, with holes in its broken roof of thatch where the rain trickled through, and never with less than two of its knotted little window-panes stopped with brown paper. The twelve or twenty pupils of both sexes who constituted the attendance sat at the two loose desks, which never fell unless you leaned on them, with an eye on the corner of the earthen floor where the worms came out, and on cold days they liked the wind to turn the peat smoke into the room. One boy, who was supposed to wash it out, got his education free for keeping the schoolhouse dirty, and the others paid their way with peats, which they brought in their hands, just as wealthier school-children carry books, and with pence which the dominie collected regularly every Monday morning. The attendance on Monday mornings was often small.

Once a year the dominie added to his income by holding cockfights in the old school. This was at Yule, and the same practice held in the parish school of Thrums. It must have been a strange sight. Every male scholar was expected to bring a cock to the school, and to pay a shilling to the dominie for the privilege of seeing it killed there. The dominie was the master of the sports, assisted by the neighbouring farmers, some of whom might be elders of the church. Three rounds were fought. By the end of the first round all the cocks had fought, and the victors were then pitted against each other. The cocks that survived the second round were eligible for the third, and the dominie, besides his shilling, got every cock killed. Sometimes, if all stories be true, the spectators were fighting with each other before the third round concluded.

The glen was but sparsely dotted with houses even in those days; a number of them inhabited by farmer-weavers, who combined two trades and just managed to live. One would have a plough, another a horse, and so in Glen Quharity they helped each other. Without a loom in addition many of them would have starved, and on Saturdays the big farmer and his wife, driving home in a gig, would pass the little farmer carrying or wheeling his wob to Thrums. When there was no longer a market for the produce of the hand-loom these farms had to be given up, and thus it is that the old school is not the only house in our weary glen around which gooseberry and currant bushes, once tended by careful hands, now grow wild.

In heavy spates the children were conveyed to the old school, as they are still to the new one, in carts, and between it and the dominie's white-washed dwelling-house swirled in winter a torrent of water that often carried lumps of the land along with it. This burn he had at times to ford on stilts.

Before the Education Act passed the dominie was not much troubled by the school inspector, who appeared in great splendour every year at Thrums. Fifteen years ago, however, Glen Quharity resolved itself into a School Board, and marched down the glen, with the minister at its head, to condemn the school. When the dominie, who had heard of their design, saw the Board approaching, he sent one of his scholars, who enjoyed making a mess of himself, wading across the burn to bring over the stilts which were lying on the other side. The Board were thus unable to send across a spokesman, and after they had harangued the dominie, who was in the best of tempers, from the wrong side of the stream, the siege was raised by their returning home, this time with the minister in the rear. So far as is known this was the only occasion on which the dominie ever lifted his hat to the minister. He was the Established Church minister at the top of the glen, but the dominie was an Auld Licht, and trudged into Thrums to church nearly every Sunday with his daughter.

The farm of Little Tilly lay so close to the dominie's house that from one window he could see

from view that led to the old school, and a dozen years ago every particle of wood about the building, including the door and the framework of the windows, had been burned by travelling tinkers.

The Board would have liked to leave the dominie in his white-washed dwelling-house to enjoy his old age comfortably, and until he learned that he had intended to retire. Then he changed his tactics and removed his beard. Instead of railing at the new school, he began to approve of it, and it soon came to the ears of the horrified Established minister, who had a man (Established) in his eye for the appointment, that the dominie was looking ten years younger. As he spurned a pension he had to get the place, and then began a warfare of bickerings between the Board and him that lasted until within a few weeks of his death. In his scholastic barn the dominie had thumped the Latin grammar into his scholars till they became university bursars to escape him. In the new school, with maps (which he hid in the hen-house) and every other modern appliance for making teaching easy, he was the scandal of the glen. He snapped at the clerk of the Board's throat, and barred his door in the minister's face. It was one of his favourite relaxations to peregrinate the district, telling the farmers who were not on the Board themselves, but were given to gossiping with those who were, that though he could slumber pleasantly in the school so long as the hum of the standards was kept up, he immediately woke if it ceased.

Having settled himself in his new quarters, the dominie seems to have read over the code, and come at once to the conclusion that it would be idle to think of straightforwardly fulfilling its requirements. The inspector he regarded as a natural enemy, who was to be circumvented by much guile. One year that admirable Oxford don arrived at the school, to find that all the children, except two girls — one of whom had her face tied up with red flannel — were away for the harvest. On another occasion the dominie met the inspector's trap some distance from the school, and explained that he would guide him by a short cut, leaving the driver to take the dog-cart to a farm where it could be put up. The unsuspecting inspector agreed, and they set off, the obsequious dominie carrying his bag. He led his victim into another glen, the hills round which had hidden their heads in mist, and then slyly remarked that he was afraid they had lost their way. The minister, who liked to attend the examination, reproved the dominie for providing no luncheon, but turned pale when his enemy suggested that he should examine the boys in Latin.

For some reason that I could never discover, the dominie had all his life refused to teach his scholars geography. The inspector and many others asked him why there was no geography class, and his invariable answer was to point to his pupils collectively, and reply in an impressive whisper —

"They winna hae her."

This story, too, seems to reflect against the dominie's views on cleanliness. One examination day the minister attended to open the inspection with prayer. Just as he was finishing, a scholar entered who had a reputation for dirt.

"Michty!" cried a little pupil, as his opening eyes fell on the apparition at the door, "there's Jocky Tamson wi' his face washed!"

When the dominie was a younger man he had first clashed with the minister during Mr. Rattray's attempts to do away with some old customs that were already dying by inches. One was the selection of a queen of beauty from among the young women at the annual Thrums fair. The judges, who were selected from the better-known farmers as a rule, sat at the door of a tent that reeked of whisky, and regarded the competitors filing by much as they selected prize sheep, with a stolid stare. There was much giggling and blushing on these occasions among the maidens, and shouts from their relatives and friends to " Haud yer head up, Jean," and " Lat them see yer een, Jess." The dominie enjoyed this, and was one time chosen a judge, when he insisted on the prize's being bestowed on his own daughter, Marget. The other judges demurred, but the dominie remained firm and won the day.

" She wasna the best-faured amon them," he admitted afterwards, " but a man maun mak the maist o' his ain."

The dominie, too, would not shake his head with Mr. Rattray over the apple and loaf bread raffles in the smithy, nor even at the Daft Days, the black week of glum debauch that ushered in the year, a period when the whole countryside rumbled to the farmer's "kebec"-laden cart.

For the great part of his career the dominie had not made forty pounds a year, but he " died worth " about three hundred pounds. The moral of his life came in just as he was leaving it, for he rose from his deathbed to hide a whisky bottle from his wife.

CHAPTER VII

CREE QUEERY AND MYSY DROLLY

THE children used to fling stones at Grinder Queery because he loved his mother. I never heard the Grinder's real name. He and his mother were Queery and Drolly, contemptuously so called, and they answered to these names. I remember Cree best as a battered old weaver, who bent forward as he walked, with his arms hanging limp as if ready to grasp the shafts of the barrow behind which it was his life to totter uphill and downhill, a rope of yarn suspended round his shaking neck, and fastened to the shafts, assisting him to bear the yoke and slowly strangling him. By and by there came a time when the barrow and the weaver seemed both palsy-stricken, and Cree, gasping for breath, would stop in the middle of a brae, unable to push his load over a stone. Then he laid himself down behind it to prevent the barrow's slipping back. On those occasions only the barefooted boys who jeered at the panting weaver could put new strength into his shrivelled arms. They did it by telling him that he

110

and Mysy would have to go to the "poorshouse" after all, at which the grey old man would wince, as if "joukin" from a blow, and, shuddering, rise and, with a desperate effort, gain the top of the incline. Small blame perhaps attached to Cree if, as he neared his grave, he grew a little dottle. His loads of yarn frequently took him past the workhouse, and his eyelids quivered as he drew near. Boys used to gather round the gate in anticipation of his coming, and make a feint of driving him inside. Cree, when he observed them, sat down on his barrow-shafts terrified to approach, and I see them now pointing to the workhouse till he left his barrow on the road and hobbled away, his legs cracking as he ran.

It is strange to know that there was once a time when Cree was young and straight, a callant who wore a flower in his buttonhole, and tried to be a hero for a maiden's sake.

Before Cree settled down as a weaver, he was knife and scissor-grinder for three counties, and Mysy, his mother, accompanied him wherever he went. Mysy trudged alongside him till her eyes grew dim and her limbs failed her, and then Cree was told that she must be sent to the pauper's home. After that a pitiable and beautiful sight was to be seen. Grinder Queery, already a feeble man, would wheel his grindstone along the long high road, leaving Mysy behind. He took the stone on a few hundred yards, and then, hiding it by the roadside in a ditch or behind a paling, returned for his mother. Her he led — sometimes he almost carried her — to the place where the grindstone lay, and thus by double journeys kept her with him. Every one said that Mysy's death would be a merciful release — every one but Cree.

Cree had been a grinder from his youth, having learned the trade from his father, but he gave it up when Mysy became almost blind. For a time he had to leave her in Thrums with Dan'l Wilkie's wife, and find employment himself in Tilliedrum. Mysy got me to write several letters for her to Cree, and she cried while telling me what to say. I never heard either of them use a term of endearment to the other, but all Mysy could tell me to put in writing was — "Oh, my son Cree; oh, my beloved son; oh, I have no one but you; oh, thou God watch over my Cree!" On one of these occasions Mysy put into my hands a paper, which, she said, would perhaps help me to write the letter. It had been drawn up by Cree many years before, when he and his mother had been compelled to part for a time, and I saw from it that he had been trying to teach Mysy to write. The paper consisted of phrases such as " Dear son Cree," " Loving mother," " I am takin' my food weel," " Yesterday," " Blankets," " The peats is near done," " Mr. Dishart," " Come home, Cree." The Grinder had left this paper with his mother, and she had written letters to him from it.

When Dan'l Wilkie objected to keeping a cranky old body like Mysy in his house Cree came back to Thrums and took a single room with a hand-loom in it. The flooring was only lumpy earth, with sacks spread over it to protect Mysy's feet. The room contained two dilapidated old coffin-beds, a dresser, a high-backed arm-chair, several three-legged stools, and two tables, of which one could be packed away beneath the other. In one corner stood the wheel at which Cree had to fill his own pirns. There was a plate-rack on one wall, and near the chimney-piece hung the wag-at-the-wall clock, the timepiece that was commonest in Thrums at that time, and that got this name because its exposed pendulum swung along the wall. The two windows in the room faced each other on opposite walls, and were so small that even a child might have stuck in trying to crawl through them. They opened on hinges, like a door. In the wall of the dark passage leading from the outer door into the room was a recess where a pan and pitcher of water always stood wedded, as it were, and a little hole, known as the "bole," in the wall opposite the fire-place contained Cree's library. It consisted of Baxter's "Saints' Rest," Harvey's "Meditations," the "Pilgrim's Progress," a work on folk-lore, and

several Bibles. The saut-backet, or salt-bucket,
stood at the end of the fender, which was half of
an old cart-wheel. Here Cree worked, whistling
"Ower the watter for Chairlie" to make Mysy
think that he was as gay as a mavis. Mysy grew
querulous in her old age, and up to the end she
thought of poor, done Cree as a handsome gallant.
Only by weaving far on into the night could Cree
earn as much as six shillings a week. He began
at six o'clock in the morning, and worked until
midnight by the light of his cruizey. The cruizey
was all the lamp Thrums had in those days,
though it is only to be seen in use now in a few
old-world houses in the glens. It is an ungainly
thing in iron, the size of a man's palm, and shaped
not unlike the palm when contracted, and deep-
ened to hold a liquid. Whale-oil, lying open in
the mould, was used, and the wick was a rash
with the green skin peeled off. These rashes
were sold by herd-boys at a halfpenny the bundle,
but Cree gathered his own wicks. The rashes
skin readily when you know how to do it. The
iron mould was placed inside another of the same
shape, but slightly larger, for in time the oil
dripped through the iron, and the whole was then
hung by a cleek or hook close to the person using
it. Even with three wicks it gave but a stime of
light, and never allowed the weaver to see more
than the half of his loom at a time. Sometimes

Cree used threads for wicks. He was too dull a man to have many visitors, but Mr. Dishart called occasionally and reproved him for telling his mother lies. The lies Cree told Mysy were that he was sharing the meals he won for her, and that he wore the overcoat which he had exchanged years before for a blanket to keep her warm.

There was a terrible want of spirit about Grinder Queery. Boys used to climb on to his stone roof with clods of damp earth in their hands, which they dropped down the chimney. Mysy was bed-ridden by this time, and the smoke threatened to choke her; so Cree, instead of chasing his persecutors, bargained with them. He gave them fly-hooks which he had busked himself, and when he had nothing left to give he tried to flatter them into dealing gently with Mysy by talking to them as men. One night it went through the town that Mysy now lay in bed all day listening for her summons to depart. According to her ideas this would come in the form of a tapping at the window, and their intention was to forestall the spirit. Dite Gow's boy, who is now a grown man, was hoisted up to one of the little windows, and he has always thought of Mysy since as he saw her then for the last time. She lay sleeping, so far as he could see, and Cree sat by the fireside looking at her.

Every one knew that there was seldom a fire in

that house unless Mysy was cold. Cree seemed
to think that the fire was getting low. In the little closet, which, with the kitchen, made up his
house, was a corner shut off from the rest of the
room by a few boards, and behind this he kept his
peats. There was a similar receptacle for potatoes
in the kitchen. Cree wanted to get another peat
for the fire without disturbing Mysy. First he
took off his boots, and made for the peats on tip-
toe. His shadow was cast on the bed, however, so
he next got down on his knees and crawled softly
into the closet. With the peat in his hands, he
returned in the same way, glancing every moment
at the bed where Mysy lay. Though Tammy
Gow's face was pressed against a broken window
he did not hear Cree putting that peat on the fire.
Some say that Mysy heard, but pretended not to
do so for her son's sake, that she realized the de-
ception he played on her, and had not the heart to
undeceive him. But it would be too sad to believe that. The boys left Cree alone that night.

The old weaver lived on alone in that solitary
house after Mysy left him, and by and by the
story went abroad that he was saving money. At
first no one believed this except the man who told
it, but there seemed after all to be something in it.
You had only to hit Cree's trouser pocket to hear
the money chinking, for he was afraid to let it out
of his clutch. Those who sat on dykes with him

when his day's labour was over said that the weaver kept his hand all the time in his pocket, and that they saw his lips move as he counted his hoard by letting it slip through his fingers. So there were boys who called "Miser Queery" after him instead of Grinder, and asked him whether he was saving up to keep himself from the workhouse.

But we had all done Cree wrong. It came out on his deathbed what he had been storing up his money for. Grinder, according to the doctor, died of getting a good meal from a friend of his earlier days after being accustomed to starve on potatoes and a very little oatmeal indeed. The day before he died this friend sent him half a sovereign, and when Grinder saw it he sat up excitedly in his bed and pulled his corduroys from beneath his pillow. The woman who, out of kindness, attended him in his last illness, looked on curiously, while Cree added the sixpences and coppers in his pocket to the half-sovereign. After all they only made some two pounds, but a look of peace came into Cree's eyes as he told the woman to take it all to a shop in the town. Nearly twelve years previously Jamie Lownie had lent him two pounds, and though the money was never asked for, it preyed on Cree's mind that he was in debt. He payed off all he owed, and so Cree's life was not, I think, a failure.

CHAPTER VIII

THE COURTING OF T'NOWHEAD'S BELL

FOR two years it had been notorious in the square that Sam'l Dickie was thinking of courting T'now-head's Bell, and that if little Sanders Elshioner (which is the Thrums pronunciation of Alexander Alexander) went in for her he might prove a formidable rival. Sam'l was a weaver in the Tenements, and Sanders a coal-carter whose trade mark was a bell on his horse's neck that told when coals were coming. Being something of a public man, Sanders had not perhaps so high a social position as Sam'l, but he had succeeded his father on the coal-cart, while the weaver had already tried several trades. It had always been against Sam'l, too, that once when the kirk was vacant he had advised the selection of the third minister who preached for it on the ground that it came expensive to pay a large number of candidates. The scandal of the thing was hushed up, out of respect for his father, who was a God-fearing man, but Sam'l was known by it in Lang Tammas's circle. The coal-carter was called Little Sanders to distinguish him from his father, who was not much more than half his size. He had grown up with the name, and its inapplicability now came home to nobody. Sam'l's mother had been more far-seeing than Sanders's. Her man had been called Sammy all his life because it was the name he got as a boy, so when their eldest son was born she spoke of him as Sam'l while still in his cradle. The neighbours imitated her, and thus the young man had a better start in life than had been granted to Sammy, his father.

It was Saturday evening — the night in the week when Auld Licht young men fell in love. Sam'l Dickie, wearing a blue glengarry bonnet with a red ball on the top, came to the door of a one-storey house in the Tenements and stood there wriggling, for he was in a suit of tweed for the first time that week, and did not feel at one with them. When his feeling of being a stranger to himself wore off he looked up and down the road, which straggles between houses and gardens, and then, picking his way over the puddles, crossed to his father's hen-house and sat down on it. He was now on his way to the square.

Eppie Fargus was sitting on an adjoining dyke knitting stockings, and Sam'l looked at her for a time.

"Is't yersel, Eppie?" he said at last.

"It's a' that," said Eppie.

"Hoo's a' wi' ye?" asked Sam'l.

"We're juist aff an' on," replied Eppie, cautiously.

There was not much more to say, but as Sam'l sidled off the henhouse he murmured politely, "Ay, ay." In another minute he would have been fairly started, but Eppie resumed the conversation.

"Sam'l," she said, with a twinkle in her eye, "ye can tell Lisbeth Fargus I'll likely be drappin' in on her aboot Mununday or Teisday."

Lisbeth was sister to Eppie, and wife of Tammas McQuhatty, better known as T'nowhead, which was the name of his farm. She was thus Bell's mistress.

Sam'l leant against the henhouse as if all his desire to depart had gone.

"Hoo d'ye kin I'll be at the T'nowhead the nicht?" he asked, grinning in anticipation.

"Ou, I'se warrant ye'll be after Bell," said Eppie.

"Am no sae sure o' that," said Sam'l, trying to leer. He was enjoying himself now.

"Am no sure o' that," he repeated, for Eppie seemed lost in stitches.

"Sam'l?"

"Ay."

"Ye'll be speirin' her sune noo, I dinna doot?"

This took Sam'l, who had only been courting Bell for a year or two, a little aback.

"Hoo d'ye mean, Eppie?" he asked.

"Maybe ye'll do't the nicht."

"Na, there's nae hurry," said Sam'l.

"Weel, we're a' coontin' on't, Sam'l."

"Gae wa wi' ye."

"What for no?"

"Gae wa wi' ye," said Sam'l again.

"Bell's gei an' fond o' ye, Sam'l."

"Ay," said Sam'l.

"But am dootin' ye're a fell billy wi' the lasses."

"Ay, oh, I d'na kin, moderate, moderate," said Sam'l, in high delight.

"I saw ye," said Eppie, speaking with a wire in her mouth, "gae'in on terr'ble wi Mysy Haggart at the pump last Saturday."

"We was juist amoosin' oorsels," said Sam'l.

"It'll be nae amoosement to Mysy," said Eppie, "gin ye brak her heart."

"Losh, Eppie," said Sam'l, "I didna think o' that."

"Ye maun kin weel, Sam'l, 'at there's mony a lass wid jump at ye."

"Ou, weel," said Sam'l, implying that a man must take these things as they come.

"For ye're a dainty chield to look at, Sam'l."

"Do ye think so, Eppie? Ay, ay; oh, I d'na kin am onything by the ordinar."

"Ye mayna be," said Eppie, "but lasses doesna do to be ower partikler."

Sam'l resented this, and prepared to depart again.

"Ye'll no tell Bell that?" he asked, anxiously.

" Tell her what ? "

" Aboot me an' Mysy."

" We'll see hoo ye behave yersel, Sam'l."

" No 'at I care, Eppie; ye can tell her gin ye like.   I widna think twice o' tellin her mysel."

" The Lord forgie ye for leein', Sam'l," said Eppie, as he disappeared down Tammy Tosh's close.   Here he came upon Henders Webster.

" Ye're late, Sam'l," said Henders.

" What for ? "

" Ou, I was thinkin' ye wid be gaen the length o' T'nowhead the nicht, an' I saw Sanders Elshioner makkin's wy there an oor syne."

" Did ye ? " cried Sam'l, adding craftily, " but it's naething to me."

" Tod, lad," said Henders, " gin ye dinna buckle to, Sanders'll be carryin' her off."

Sam'l flung back his head and passed on.

" Sam'l ! " cried Henders after him.

" Ay," said Sam'l, wheeling round.

" Gie Bell a kiss frae me."

The full force of this joke struck neither all at once.   Sam'l began to smile at it as he turned down the school-wynd, and it came upon Henders while he was in his garden feeding his ferret.   Then he slapped his legs gleefully, and explained the conceit to Will'um Byars, who went into the house and thought it over.

There were twelve or twenty little groups of

men in the square, which was lit by a flare of oil suspended over a cadger's cart. Now and again a staid young woman passed through the square with a basket on her arm, and if she had lingered long enough to give them time, some of the idlers would have addressed her. As it was, they gazed after her, and then grinned to each other.

"Ay, Sam'l," said two or three young men, as Sam'l joined them beneath the town clock.

"Ay, Davit," replied Sam'l.

This group was composed of some of the sharpest wits in Thrums, and it was not to be expected that they would let this opportunity pass. Perhaps when Sam'l joined them he knew what was in store for him.

"Was ye lookin' for T'nowhead's Bell, Sam'l?" asked one.

"Or mebbe ye was wantin' the minister?" suggested another, the same who had walked out twice with Chirsty Duff and not married her after all.

Sam'l could not think of a good reply at the moment, so he laughed good-naturedly.

"Ondoobtedly she's a snod bit crittur," said Davit, archly.

"An' michty clever wi' her fingers," added Jamie Deuchars.

"Man, I've thocht o' makkin' up to Bell mysel," said Pete Ogle. "Wid there be ony chance, think ye, Sam'l?"

" I'm thinkin' she widna hae ye for her first, Pete," replied Sam'l, in one of those happy flashes that come to some men, "but there's nae sayin' but what she micht tak ye to finish up wi.' "

The unexpectedness of this sally startled every one. Though Sam'l did not set up for a wit, however, like Davit, it was notorious that he could say a cutting thing once in a way.

"Did ye ever see Bell reddin up ? " asked Pete, recovering from his overthrow. He was a man who bore no malice.

" It's a sicht," said Sam'l, solemnly.

" Hoo will that be ? " asked Jamie Deuchars.

" It's weel worth yer while," said Pete, " to ging atower to the T'nowhead an' see. Ye'll mind the closed-in beds i' the kitchen ? Ay, weel, they're a fell spoilt crew, T'nowhead's litlins, an' no that aisy to manage. Th' ither lasses Lisbeth's hae'n had a michty trouble wi' them. When they war i' the middle o' their reddin up the bairns wid come tumlin' about the floor, but, sal, I assure ye, Bell didna fash lang wi' them. Did she, Sam'l ? "

" She did not," said Sam'l, dropping into a fine mode of speech to add emphasis to his remark.

" I'll tell ye what she did," said Pete to the others. " She juist lifted up the litlins, twa at a time, an' flung them into the coffin-beds. Syne she snibbit the doors on them, an' keepit them there till the floor was dry."

124

" Ay, man, did she so ? " said Davit, admiringly.

" I've seen her do't mysel," said Sam'l.

" There's no a lassie maks better bannocks this side o' Fetter Lums," continued Pete.

" Her mither tocht her that," said Sam'l; "she was a gran' han' at the bakin', Kitty Ogilvy."

"I've heard say," remarked Jamie, putting it this way so as not to tie himself down to anything, "'at Bell's scones is equal to Mag Lunan's."

" So they are," said Sam'l, almost fiercely.

" I kin she's a neat han' at singein' a hen," said Pete.

"An' wi't a'," said Davit, " she's a snod, canty bit stocky in her Sabbath claes."

" If onything, thick in the waist," suggested Jamie.

" I dinna see that," said Sam'l.

" I d'na care for her hair either," continued Jamie, who was very nice in his tastes; "something mair yallowchy wid be an improvement."

" A'body kins," growled Sam'l, " 'at black hair's the bonniest."

The others chuckled.

" Puir Sam'l ! " Pete said.

Sam'l not being certain whether this should be received with a smile or a frown, opened his mouth wide as a kind of compromise. This was position one with him for thinking things over.

Few Auld Lichts, as I have said, went the length

of choosing a helpmate for themselves. One day a young man's friends would see him mending the washing tub of a maiden's mother. They kept the joke until Saturday night, and then he learned from them what he had been after. It dazed him for a time, but in a year or so he grew accustomed to the idea, and they were then married. With a little help he fell in love just like other people.

Sam'l was going the way of the others, but he found it difficult to come to the point. He only went courting once a week, and he could never take up the running at the place where he left off the Saturday before. Thus he had not, so far, made great headway. His method of making up to Bell had been to drop in at T'nowhead on Saturday nights and talk with the farmer about the rinderpest.

The farm kitchen was Bell's testimonial. Its chairs, tables, and stools were scoured by her to the whiteness of Rob Angus's sawmill boards, and the muslin blind on the window was starched like a child's pinafore. Bell was brave, too, as well as energetic. Once Thrums had been overrun with thieves. It is now thought that there may have been only one, but he had the wicked cleverness of a gang. Such was his repute that there were weavers who spoke of locking their doors when they went from home. He was not very skilful, however, being generally caught, and when they said they knew he was a robber he gave them their things back and went away. If they had given him time there is no doubt that he would have gone off with his plunder. One night he went to T'nowhead, and Bell, who slept in the kitchen, was wakened by the noise. She knew who it would be, so she rose and dressed herself, and went to look for him with a candle. The thief had not known what to do when he got in, and as it was very lonely he was glad to see Bell. She told him he ought to be ashamed of himself, and would not let him out by the door until he had taken off his boots so as not to soil the carpet.

On this Saturday evening Sam'l stood his ground in the square, until by and by he found himself alone. There were other groups there still, but his circle had melted away. They went separately, and no one said good-night. Each took himself off slowly, backing out of the group until he was fairly started.

Sam'l looked about him, and then, seeing that the others had gone, walked round the townhouse into the darkness of the brae that leads down and then up to the farm of T'nowhead.

To get into the good graces of Lisbeth Fargus you had to know her ways and humour them. Sam'l, who was a student of women, knew this, and so, instead of pushing the door open and walking in, he went through the rather ridiculous ceremony of knocking. Sanders Elshioner was also aware of this weakness of Lisbeth's, but, though he often made up his mind to knock, the absurdity of the thing prevented his doing so when he reached the door. T'nowhead himself had never got used to his wife's refined notions, and when any one knocked he always started to his feet, thinking there must be something wrong.

Lisbeth came to the door, her expansive figure blocking the way in.

"Sam'l," she said.

"Lisbeth," said Sam'l.

He shook hands with the farmer's wife, knowing that she liked it, but only said, "Ay, Bell," to his sweetheart, "Ay, T'nowhead," to McQuhatty, and "It's yersel, Sanders," to his rival.

They were all sitting round the fire, T'nowhead, with his feet on the ribs, wondering why he felt so warm, and Bell darned a stocking, while Lisbeth kept an eye on a goblet full of potatoes.

"Sit into the fire, Sam'l," said the farmer, not, however, making way for him.

"Na, na," said Sam'l, "I'm to bide nae time." Then he sat into the fire. His face was turned away from Bell, and when she spoke he answered her without looking round. Sam'l felt a little anxious. Sanders Elshioner, who had one leg shorter than the other, but looked well when sitting, seemed suspiciously at home. He asked Bell

questions out of his own head, which was beyond
Sam'l, and once he said something to her in such
a low voice that the others could not catch it.
T'nowhead asked curiously what it was, and Sanders explained that he had only said, "Ay, Bell,
the morn's the Sabbath." There was nothing
startling in this, but Sam'l did not like it. He
began to wonder if he was too late, and had he
seen his opportunity would have told Bell of a
nasty rumour that Sanders intended to go over to
the Free Church if they would make him kirk-
officer.

Sam'l had the good-will of T'nowhead's wife,
who liked a polite man. Sanders did his best, but
from want of practice he constantly made mistakes.
To-night, for instance, he wore his hat in the house
because he did not like to put up his hand and
take it off. T'nowhead had not taken his off
either, but that was because he meant to go out
by and by and lock the byre door. It was impossible to say which of her lovers Bell preferred.
The proper course with an Auld Licht lassie was
to prefer the man who proposed to her.

"Ye'll bide a wee, an' hae something to eat?"
Lisbeth asked Sam'l, with her eyes on the goblet.

"No, I thank ye," said Sam'l, with true gen-
teelity.

"Ye'll better?"

"I dinna think it."

"Hoots aye; what's to hender ye?"

"Weel, since ye're sae pressin', I'll bide."

No one asked Sanders to stay. Bell could not, for she was but the servant, and T'nowhead knew that the kick his wife had given him meant that he was not to do so either. Sanders whistled to show that he was not uncomfortable.

"Ay, then, I'll be stappin' ower the brae," he said at last.

He did not go, however. There was sufficient pride in him to get him off his chair, but only slowly, for he had to get accustomed to the notion of going. At intervals of two or three minutes he remarked that he must now be going. In the same circumstances Sam'l would have acted similarly. For a Thrums man it is one of the hardest things in life to get away from anywhere.

At last Lisbeth saw that something must be done. The potatoes were burning, and T'nowhead had an invitation on his tongue.

"Yes, I'll hae to be movin'," said Sanders, hopelessly, for the fifth time.

"Guid nicht to ye, then, Sanders," said Lisbeth. "Gie the door a fling-to, ahent ye."

Sanders, with a mighty effort, pulled himself together. He looked boldly at Bell, and then took off his hat carefully. Sam'l saw with misgivings that there was something in it which was not a handkerchief. It was a paper bag glittering with

130

gold braid, and contained such an assortment of sweets as lads bought for their lasses on the Muckle Friday.

"Hae, Bell," said Sanders, handing the bag to Bell in an off-hand way as if it were but a trifle. Nevertheless he was a little excited, for he went off without saying good-night.

No one spoke. Bell's face was crimson. T'nowhead fidgetted on his chair, and Lisbeth looked at Sam'l. The weaver was strangely calm and collected, though he would have liked to know whether this was a proposal.

"Sit in by to the table, Sam'l," said Lisbeth, trying to look as if things were as they had been before.

She put a saucerful of butter, salt, and pepper near the fire to melt, for melted butter is the shoeing-horn that helps over a meal of potatoes. Sam'l, however, saw what the hour required, and jumping up, he seized his bonnet.

"Hing the tatties higher up the joist, Lisbeth," he said with dignity; "I'se be back in ten meenits."

He hurried out of the house, leaving the others looking at each other.

"What do ye think?" asked Lisbeth.

"I d'na kin," faltered Bell.

"Thae tatties is lang o' comin' to the boil," said T'nowhead.

In some circles a lover who behaved like Sam'l would have been suspected of intent upon his rival's life, but neither Bell nor Lisbeth did the weaver that injustice. In a case of this kind it does not much matter what T'nowhead thought.

The ten minutes had barely passed when Sam'l was back in the farm kitchen. He was too flurried to knock this time, and, indeed, Lisbeth did not expect it of him.

"Bell, hae!" he cried, handing his sweetheart a tinsel bag twice the size of Sanders's gift.

"Losh preserve's!" exclaimed Lisbeth; "I'se warrant there's a shillin's worth."

"There's a' that, Lisbeth — an' mair," said Sam'l, firmly.

"I thank ye, Sam'l," said Bell, feeling an unwonted elation as she gazed at the two paper bags in her lap.

"Ye're ower extravegint, Sam'l," Lisbeth said.

"Not at all," said Sam'l; "not at all. But I widna advise ye to eat thae ither anes, Bell — they're second quality."

Bell drew back a step from Sam'l.

"How do ye kin?" asked the farmer shortly, for he liked Sanders.

"I spiered i' the shop," said Sam'l.

The goblet was placed on a broken plate on the table with the saucer beside it, and Sam'l, like the others, helped himself. What he did was to take potatoes from the pot with his fingers, peel off their coats, and then dip them into the butter. Lisbeth would have liked to provide knives and forks, but she knew that beyond a certain point T'nowhead was master in his own house. As for Sam'l, he felt victory in his hands, and began to think that he had gone too far.

In the meantime Sanders, little witting that Sam'l had trumped his trick, was sauntering along the kirk-wynd, with his hat on the side of his head. Fortunately he did not meet the minister.

The courting of T'nowhead's Bell reached its crisis one Sabbath about a month after the events above recorded. The minister was in great force that day, but it is no part of mine to tell how he bore himself. I was there, and am not likely to forget the scene. It was a fateful Sabbath for T'nowhead's Bell and her swains, and destined to be remembered for the painful scandal which they perpetrated in their passion.

Bell was not in the kirk. There being an infant of six months in the house it was a question of either Lisbeth or the lassie's staying at home with him, and though Lisbeth was unselfish in a general way, she could not resist the delight of going to church. She had nine children besides the baby, and being but a woman, it was the pride of her life to march them into the T'nowhead pew, so well watched that they dared not misbehave, and so tightly packed that they could not fall. The congregation looked at that pew, the mothers enviously, when they sang the lines —

> " Jerusalem like a city is
> Compactly built together."

The first half of the service had been gone through on this particular Sunday without anything remarkable happening. It was at the end of the psalm which preceded the sermon that Sanders Elshioner, who sat near the door, lowered his head until it was no higher than the pews, and in that attitude, looking almost like a four-footed animal, slipped out of the church. In their eagerness to be at the sermon many of the congregation did not notice him, and those who did put the matter by in their minds for future investigation. Sam'l, however, could not take it so coolly. From his seat in the gallery he saw Sanders disappear, and his mind misgave him. With the true lover's instinct he understood it all. Sanders had been struck by the fine turn-out in the T'nowhead pew. Bell was alone at the farm. What an opportunity to work one's way up to a proposal. T'nowhead was so overrun with children that such a chance seldom occurred, except on a Sabbath. Sanders, doubtless, was off to propose, and he, Sam'l, was left behind.

The suspense was terrible. Sam'l and Sanders

had both known all along that Bell would take the
first of the two who asked her. Even those who
thought her proud admitted that she was modest.
Bitterly the weaver repented having waited so
long. Now it was too late. In ten minutes
Sanders would be at T'nowhead; in an hour all
would be over. Sam'l rose to his feet in a daze.
His mother pulled him down by the coat-tail, and
his father shook him, thinking he was walking in
his sleep. He tottered past them, however, hurried
up the aisle, which was so narrow that Dan'l Ross
could only reach his seat by walking sideways,
and was gone before the minister could do more
than stop in the middle of a whirl and gape in
horror after him.

A number of the congregation felt that day the
advantage of sitting in the laft. What was a
mystery to those downstairs was revealed to them.
From the gallery windows they had a fine open
view to the south; and as Sam'l took the common, which was a short cut though a steep as-
cent, to T'nowhead, he was never out of their line
of vision. Sanders was not to be seen, but they
guessed rightly the reason why. Thinking he had
ample time, he had gone round by the main road
to save his boots—perhaps a little scared by what
was coming. Sam'l's design was to forestall him
by taking the shorter path over the burn and up
the commonty.

It was a race for a wife, and several on-lookers in the gallery braved the minister's displeasure to see who won. Those who favoured Sam'l's suit exultingly saw him leap the stream, while the friends of Sanders fixed their eyes on the top of the common where it ran into the road. Sanders must come into sight there, and the one who reached this point first would get Bell.

As Auld Lichts do not walk abroad on the Sabbath, Sanders would probably not be delayed. The chances were in his favour. Had it been any other day in the week Sam'l might have run. So some of the congregation in the gallery were thinking, when suddenly they saw him bend low and then take to his heels. He had caught sight of Sanders's head bobbing over the hedge that separated the road from the common, and feared that Sanders might see him. The congregation who could crane their necks sufficiently saw a black object, which they guessed to be the carter's hat, crawling along the hedge-top. For a moment it was motionless, and then it shot ahead. The rivals had seen each other. It was now a hot race. Sam'l, dissembling no longer, clattered up the common, becoming smaller and smaller to the onlookers as he neared the top. More than one person in the gallery almost rose to their feet in their excitement. Sam'l had it. No, Sanders was in front. Then the two figures disappeared from view. They seemed to run into each other at the top of the brae, and no one could say who was first. The congregation looked at one another. Some of them perspired. But the minister held on his course.

Sam'l had just been in time to cut Sanders out. It was the weaver's saving that Sanders saw this when his rival turned the corner; for Sam'l was sadly blown. Sanders took in the situation and gave in at once. The last hundred yards of the distance he covered at his leisure, and when he arrived at his destination he did not go in. It was a fine afternoon for the time of year, and he went round to have a look at the pig, about which T'nowhead was a little sinfully puffed up.

"Ay," said Sanders, digging his fingers critically into the grunting animal; "quite so."

"Grumph," said the pig, getting reluctantly to his feet.

"Ou ay; yes," said Sanders, thoughtfully.

Then he sat down on the edge of the sty, and looked long and silently at an empty bucket. But whether his thoughts were of T'nowhead's Bell, whom he had lost for ever, or of the food the farmer fed his pig on, is not known.

"Lord preserve's! Are ye no at the kirk?" cried Bell, nearly dropping the baby as Sam'l broke into the room.

"Bell!" cried Sam'l.

137

Then T'nowhead's Bell knew that her hour had come.

"Sam'l," she faltered.

"Will ye hae's Bell?" demanded Sam'l, glaring at her sheepishly.

"Ay," answered Bell.

Sam'l fell into a chair.

"Bring's a drink o' water, Bell," he said.

But Bell thought the occasion required milk, and there was none in the kitchen. She went out to the byre, still with the baby in her arms, and saw Sanders Elshioner sitting gloomily on the pigsty.

"Weel, Bell," said Sanders.

"I thocht ye'd been at the kirk, Sanders," said Bell.

Then there was a silence between them.

"Has Sam'l spiered ye, Bell?" asked Sanders, stolidly.

"Ay," said Bell again, and this time there was a tear in her eye. Sanders was little better than an "orra man," and Sam'l was a weaver, and yet —— But it was too late now. Sanders gave the pig a vicious poke with a stick, and when it had ceased to grunt, Bell was back in the kitchen. She had forgotten about the milk, however, and Sam'l only got water after all.

In after days, when the story of Bell's wooing was told, there were some who held that the cir-

cumstances would have almost justified the lassie
in giving Sam'l the go-by. But these perhaps forgot that her other lover was in the same predicament as the accepted one — that of the two, indeed, he was the more to blame, for he set off to
T'nowhead on the Sabbath of his own accord,
while Sam'l only ran after him. And then there
is no one to say for certain whether Bell heard of
her suitors' delinquencies until Lisbeth's return
from the kirk. Sam'l could never remember
whether he told her, and Bell was not sure
whether, if he did, she took it in. Sanders was
greatly in demand for weeks after to tell what he
knew of the affair, but though he was twice asked
to tea to the manse among the trees, and subjected
thereafter to ministerial cross-examinations, this is
all he told. He remained at the pigsty until
Sam'l left the farm, when he joined him at the
top of the brae, and they went home together.

"It's yersel, Sanders," said Sam'l.

"It is so, Sam'l," said Sanders.

"Very cauld," said Sam'l.

"Blawy," assented Sanders.

After a pause —

"Sam'l," said Sanders.

"Ay."

"I'm hearin' yer to be mairit."

"Ay."

"Weel, Sam'l, she's a snod bit lassie."

" Thank ye," said Sam'l.

" I had ance a kin' o' notion o' Bell mysel," continued Sanders.

" Ye had ? "

" Yes, Sam'l; but I thocht better o't."

" Hoo d'ye mean ? " asked Sam'l, a little anxiously.

" Weel, Sam'l, mairitch is a terrible responsibeelity."

" It is so," said Sam'l, wincing.

" An' no the thing to tak up withoot conseederation."

" But it's a blessed and honourable state, Sanders; ye've heard the minister on't."

" They say," continued the relentless Sanders, " 'at the minister doesna get on sair wi' the wife himsel."

" So they do," cried Sam'l, with a sinking at the heart.

" I've been telt," Sanders went on, " 'at gin ye can get the upper han' o' the wife for a while at first, there's the mair chance o' a harmonious exeestence."

" Bell's no the lassie," said Sam'l, appealingly, " to thwart her man."

Sanders smiled.

" D' ye think she is, Sanders ? "

" Weel, Sam'l, I d'na want to fluster ye, but she's been ower lang wi' Lisbeth Fargus no to hae learnt her ways. An a'body kins what a life T'nowhead has wi' her."

"Guid sake, Sanders, hoo did ye no speak o' this afore?"

"I thocht ye kent o't, Sam'l."

They had now reached the square, and the U. P. kirk was coming out. The Auld Licht kirk would be half an hour yet.

"But, Sanders," said Sam'l, brightening up, "ye was on yer way to spier her yersel."

"I was, Sam'l," said Sanders, "and I canna but be thankfu ye was ower quick for's."

"Gin't hadna been you," said Sam'l, "I wid never hae thocht o't."

"I'm sayin' naething agin Bell," pursued the other, "but, man Sam'l, a body should be mair deleeberate in a thing o' the kind."

"It was michty hurried," said Sam'l, woefully.

"It's a serious thing to spier a lassie," said Sanders.

"It's an awfu thing," said Sam'l.

"But we'll hope for the best," added Sanders, in a hopeless voice.

They were close to the Tenements now, and Sam'l looked as if he were on his way to be hanged.

"Sam'l?"

"Ay, Sanders."

"Did ye — did ye kiss her, Sam'l?"

"Na."

"Hoo?"

"There's was varra little time, Sanders."

"Half an 'oor," said Sanders.

"Was there? Man Sanders, to tell ye the truth, I never thocht o't."

Then the soul of Sanders Elshioner was filled with contempt for Sam'l Dickie.

The scandal blew over. At first it was expected that the minister would interfere to prevent the union, but beyond intimating from the pulpit that the souls of Sabbath-breakers were beyond praying for, and then praying for Sam'l and Sanders at great length, with a word thrown in for Bell, he let things take their course. Some said it was because he was always frightened lest his young men should intermarry with other denominations, but Sanders explained it differently to Sam'l.

"I hav'na a word to say agin the minister," he said; "they're gran' prayers, but Sam'l, he's a mairit man himsel."

"He's a' the better for that, Sanders, is'na he?"

"Do ye no see," asked Sanders, compassionately, "'at he's tryin' to mak the best o't?"

"Oh, Sanders, man!" said Sam'l.

"Cheer up, Sam'l," said Sanders, "it'll sune be ower."

Their having been rival suitors had not interfered with their friendship. On the contrary, while they had hitherto been mere acquaintances, they became inseparables as the wedding-day drew near. It was noticed that they had much to say to each other, and that when they could not get a room to themselves they wandered about together in the churchyard. When Sam'l had anything to tell Bell he sent Sanders to tell it, and Sanders did as he was bid. There was nothing that he would not have done for Sam'l.

The more obliging Sanders was, however, the sadder Sam'l grew. He never laughed now on Saturdays, and sometimes his loom was silent half the day. Sam'l felt that Sanders's was the kindness of a friend for a dying man.

It was to be a penny wedding, and Lisbeth Fargus said it was delicacy that made Sam'l superintend the fitting-up of the barn by deputy. Once he came to see it in person, but he looked so ill that Sanders had to see him home. This was on the Thursday afternoon, and the wedding was fixed for Friday.

"Sanders, Sanders," said Sam'l, in a voice strangely unlike his own, "it'll a' be ower by this time the morn."

"It will," said Sanders.

"If I had only kent her langer," continued Sam'l.

"It wid hae been safer," said Sanders.

"Did ye see the yallow floor in Bell's bonnet?" asked the accepted swain.

143

" Ay," said Sanders, reluctantly.

" I'm dootin' — I'm sair dootin' she's but a flichty, licht-hearted crittur after a'."

" I had ay my suspeecions o't," said Sanders.

" Ye hae kent her langer than me," said Sam'l.

" Yes," said Sanders, " but there's nae gettin' at the heart o' women. Man, Sam'l, they're desperate cunnin'."

" I'm dootin't; I'm sair dootin't."

" It'll be a warnin' to ye, Sam'l, no to be in sic a hurry i' the futur," said Sanders.

Sam'l groaned.

" Ye'll be gaein up to the manse to arrange wi' the minister the morn's mornin'," continued Sanders in a subdued voice.

Sam'l looked wistfully at his friend.

" I canna do't, Sanders," he said, " I canna do't."

" Ye maun," said Sanders.

" It's aisy to speak," retorted Sam'l, bitterly.

" We have a' oor troubles, Sam'l," said Sanders, soothingly, " an' every man maun bear his ain burdens. Johnny Davie's wife's dead, an' he's no repinin'."

" Ay," said Sam'l, " but a death's no a mairitch. We hae haen deaths in our family too."

" It may a' be for the best," added Sanders, " an' there wid be a michty talk i' the hale country-side gin ye didna ging to the minister like a man."

" I maun hae langer to think o't," said Sam'l.

"Bell's mairitch is the morn," said Sanders, decisively.

Sam'l glanced up with a wild look in his eyes.

"Sanders," he cried.

"Sam'l?"

"Ye hae been a guid friend to me, Sanders, in this sair affliction."

"Nothing ava," said Sanders; "dount mention'd."

"But, Sanders, ye canna deny but what your rinnin oot o' the kirk that awfu' day was at the bottom o'd a'."

"It was so," said Sanders, bravely.

"An' ye used to be fond o' Bell, Sanders."

"I dinna deny't."

"Sanders, laddie," said Sam'l, bending forward and speaking in a wheedling voice, "I aye thocht it was you she likeit."

"I had some sic idea mysel," said Sanders.

"Sanders, I canna think to pairt twa fowk sae weel suited to ane anither as you an' Bell."

"Canna ye, Sam'l?"

"She wid mak ye a guid wife, Sanders. I hae studied her weel, and she's a thrifty, douce, clever lassie. Sanders, there's no the like o' her. Mony a time, Sanders, I hae said to mysel, There's a lass ony man micht be prood to tak. A'body says the same, Sanders. There's nae risk ava, man: nane to speak o'. Tak her, laddie, tak her, Sanders;

it's a grand chance, Sanders. She's yours for the spierin. I'll gie her up, Sanders."

" Will ye, though ? " said Sanders.

" What d'ye think ? " asked Sam'l.

" If ye wid rayther," said Sanders, politely.

" There's my han' on't," said Sam'l. " Bless ye, Sanders ; ye've been a true frien' to me."

Then they shook hands for the first time in their lives ; and soon afterwards Sanders struck up the brae to T'nowhead.

Next morning Sanders Elshioner, who had been very busy the night before, put on his Sabbath clothes and strolled up to the manse.

" But — but where is Sam'l ? " asked the minister ; " I must see himself."

" It's a new arrangement," said Sanders.

" What do you mean, Sanders ? "

" Bell's to marry me," explained Sanders.

" But — but what does Sam'l say ? "

" He's willin'," said Sanders.

" And Bell ? "

" She's willin', too. She prefers't."

" It is unusual," said the minister.

" It's a' richt," said Sanders.

" Well, you know best," said the minister.

" You see the hoose was taen, at ony rate," continued Sanders. " An I'll juist ging in til't instead o' Sam'l."

" Quite so."

" An' I cudna think to disappoint the lassie."

" Your sentiments do you credit, Sanders," said the minister; " but I hope you do not enter upon the blessed state of matrimony without full consideration of its responsibilities. It is a serious business, marriage."

" It's a' that," said Sanders, " but I'm willin' to stan' the risk."

So, as soon as it could be done, Sanders Elshioner took to wife T'nowhead's Bell, and I remember seeing Sam'l Dickie trying to dance at the penny wedding.

Years afterwards it was said in Thrums that Sam'l had treated Bell badly, but he was never sure about it himself.

" It was a near thing — a michty near thing," he admitted in the square.

" They say," some other weaver would remark, " 'at it was you Bell liked best."

" I d'na kin," Sam'l would reply, " but there's nae doot the lassie was fell fond o' me. Ou, a mere passin' fancy's ye micht say."

CHAPTER IX

When an election-day comes round now, it takes me back to the time of 1832. I would be eight or ten year old at the time. James Strachan was at the door by five o'clock in the morning in his Sabbath clothes, by arrangement. We was to go up to the hill to see them building the bonfire. Moreover, there was word that Mr. Scrimgour was to be there tossing pennies, just like at a marriage. I was wakened before that by my mother at the pans and bowls. I have always associated elections since that time with jelly-making; for just as my mother would fill the cups and tankers and bowls with jelly to save cans, she was emptying the pots and pans to make way for the ale and porter. James and me was to help to carry it home from the square — him in the pitcher and me in a flagon, because I was silly for my age and not strong in the arms.

It was a very blowy morning, though the rain kept off, and what part of the bonfire had been built already was found scattered to the winds.

148

Before we rose a great mass of folk was getting
the barrels and things together again; but some
of them was never recovered, and suspicion pointed
to William Geddes, it being well known that William would not hesitate to carry off anything if unobserved. More by token Chirsty Lamby had seen
him rolling home a barrowful of firewood early in
the morning, her having risen to hold cold water
in her mouth, being down with the toothache.
When we got up to the hill everybody was making for the quarry, which being more sheltered was
now thought to be a better place for the bonfire.
The masons had struck work, it being a general
holiday in the whole country-side. There was a
great commotion of people, all fine dressed and
mostly with glengarry bonnets; and me and James
was well acquaint with them, though mostly weavers and the like and not my father's equal. Mr.
Scrimgour was not there himself; but there was a
small active body in his room as tossed the money
for him fair enough; though not so liberally as was
expected, being mostly ha'pence where pennies
was looked for. Such was not my father's opinion, and him and a few others only had a vote.
He considered it was a waste of money giving to
them that had no vote and so taking out of other
folks' mouths, but the little man said it kept everybody in good-humour and made Mr. Scrimgour
popular. He was an extraordinary affable man

and very spirity, running about to waste no time
in walking, and gave me a shilling, saying to me
to be a truthful boy and tell my father. He did
not give James anything, him being an orphan,
but clapped his head and said he was a fine boy.

The Captain was to vote for the Bill if he got
in, the which he did. It was the Captain was to
give the ale and porter in the square like a true
gentleman. My father gave a kind of laugh when
I let him see my shilling, and said he would keep
care of it for me; and sorry I was I let him get it,
me never seeing the face of it again to this day.
Me and James was much annoyed with the women, especially Kitty Davie, always pushing in
when there was tossing, and tearing the very ha'-
pence out of our hands: us not caring so much
about the money, but humiliated to see women
mixing up in politics. By the time the topmost
barrel was on the bonfire there was a great smell
of whisky in the quarry, it being a confined place.
My father had been against the bonfire being in
the quarry, arguing that the wind on the hill
would have carried off the smell of the whisky;
but Peter Tosh said they did not want the smell
carried off; it would be agreeable to the masons
for weeks to come. Except among the women
there was no fighting nor wrangling at the quarry
but all in fine spirits.

I misremember now whether it was Mr. Scrimgour or the Captain that took the fancy to my father's pigs; but it was this day, at any rate, that the Captain sent him the gamecock. Whichever one it was that fancied the litter of pigs, nothing would content him but to buy them, which he did at thirty shillings each, being the best bargain ever my father made. Nevertheless I'm thinking he was windier of the cock. The Captain, who was a local man when not with his regiment, had the grandest collection of fighting-cocks in the county, and sometimes came into the town to try them against the town cocks. I mind well the large wicker cage in which they were conveyed from place to place, and never without the Captain near at hand. My father had a cock that beat all the other town cocks at the cock fight at our school, which was superintended by the elder of the kirk to see fair play; but the which died of its wounds the next day but one. This was a great grief to my father, it having been challenged to fight the Captain's cock. Therefore it was very considerate of the Captain to make my father a present of his bird; father, in compliment to him, changing its name from the " Deil " to the " Captain."

During the forenoon, and I think until well on in the day, James and me was busy with the pitcher and the flagon. The proceedings in the square, however, was not so well conducted as in the quarry, many of the folk there assembled show-

ing a mean and grasping spirit. The Captain had
given orders that there was to be no stint of ale
and porter, and neither there was; but much of it
lost through hastiness. Great barrels was hurled
into the middle of the square, where the country
wives sat with their eggs and butter on market-
day, and was quickly stove in with an axe or paving-stone or whatever came handy. Sometimes
they would break into the barrel at different
points; and then, when they tilted it up to get
the ale out at one hole, it gushed out at the bottom till the square was flooded. My mother was
fair disgusted when told by me and James of the
waste of good liquor. It is gospel truth I speak
when I say I mind well of seeing Singer Davie
catching the porter in a pan as it ran down the
sire, and, when the pan was full to overflowing,
putting his mouth to the stream and drinking till
he was as full as the pan. Most of the men, however, stuck to the barrels, the drink running in the
street being ale and porter mixed, and left it to the
women and the young folk to do the carrying. Susy
M'Queen brought as many pans as she could collect
on a barrow, and was filling them all with porter, re-
jecting the ale; but indignation was aroused against
her, and as fast as she filled, the others emptied.

My father scorned to go to the square to drink
ale and porter with the crowd, having the election
on his mind and him to vote. Nevertheless he

instructed me and James to keep up a brisk trade with the pans, and run back across the gardens in case we met dishonest folk in the streets who might drink the ale. Also, said my father, we was to let the excesses of our neighbours be a warning in sobriety to us; enough being as good as a feast, except when you can store it up for the winter. By and by my mother thought it was not safe me being in the streets with so many wild men about, and would have sent James himself, him being an orphan and hardier; but this I did not like, but, running out, did not come back for long enough. There is no doubt that the music was to blame for firing the men's blood, and the result most disgraceful fighting with no object in view. There was three fiddlers and two at the flute, most of them blind, but not the less dangerous on that account; and they kept the town in a ferment, even playing the countryfolk home to the farms, followed by bands of townsfolk. They were a quarrelsome set, the ploughmen and others; and it was generally admitted in the town that their overbearing behaviour was responsible for the fights. I mind them being driven out of the square, stones flying thick; also some stand-up fights with sticks, and others fair enough with fists. The worst fight I did not see. It took place in a field. At first it was only between two who had been miscalling one another; but there was many looking on, and when the town man was like getting the worst of it the others set to, and a most heathenish fray with no sense in it ensued. One man had his arm broken. I mind Hobart the bellman going about ringing his bell and telling all persons to get within doors; but little attention was paid to him, it being notorious that Snecky had had a fight earlier in the day himself.

When James was fighting in the field, according to his own account, I had the honour of dining with the electors who voted for the Captain, him paying all expenses. It was a lucky accident my mother sending me to the town-house, where the dinner came off, to try to get my father home at a decent hour, me having a remarkable power over him when in liquor but at no other time. They were very jolly, however, and insisted on my drinking the Captain's health and eating more than was safe. My father got it next day from my mother for this; and so would I myself, but it was several days before I left my bed, completely knocked up as I was with the excitement and one thing or another. The bonfire, which was built to celebrate the election of Mr. Scrimgour, was set ablaze, though I did not see it, in honour of the election of the Captain; it being thought a pity to lose it, as no doubt it would have been. That is about all I remember of the celebrated election of '32 when the Reform Bill was passed.

CHAPTER X

A VERY OLD FAMILY

THEY were a very old family with whom Snecky Hobart, the bellman, lodged. Their favourite dissipation, when their looms had come to rest, was a dander through the kirkyard. They dressed for it: the three young ones in their rusty black; the patriarch in his old blue coat, velvet knee-breeches, and broad blue bonnet; and often of an evening I have met them moving from grave to grave. By this time the old man was nearly ninety, and the young ones averaged sixty. They read out the inscriptions on the tombstones in a solemn drone, and their father added his reminiscences. He never failed them. Since the beginning of the century he had not missed a funeral, and his children felt that he was a great example. Sire and sons returned from the cemetery invigorated for their daily labours. If one of them happened to start a dozen yards behind the others, he never thought of making up the distance. If his foot struck against a stone, he came to a dead-stop; when he discovered that he had stopped, he set off again.

A high wall shut off this old family's house and garden from the clatter of Thrums, a wall that gave Snecky some trouble before he went to live within it. I speak from personal knowledge. One spring morning, before the schoolhouse was built, I was assisting the patriarch to divest the gaunt garden pump of its winter suit of straw. I was taking a drink, I remember, my palm over the mouth of the wooden spout and my mouth at the gimlet hole above, when a leg appeared above the corner of the wall against which the henhouse was built. Two hands followed, clutching desperately at the uneven stones. Then the leg worked as if it were turning a grind-stone, and next moment Snecky was sitting breathlessly on the dyke. From this to the henhouse, whose roof was of "divets," the descent was comparatively easy, and a slanting board allowed the daring bellman to slide thence to the ground. He had come on business, and having talked it over slowly with the old man he turned to depart. Though he was a genteel man, I heard him sigh heavily as, with the remark, " Ay, weel, I'll be movin' again," he began to rescale the wall. The patriarch, twisted round the pump, made no reply, so I ventured to suggest to the bellman that he might find the gate easier. " Is there a gate? " said Snecky, in surprise at the resources of civilization. I pointed it out to him, and he went his way chuckling. The old man told me that he had sometimes wondered at Snecky's mode of approach, but it had not struck him to say anything. Afterwards, when the bellman took up his abode there, they discussed the matter heavily.

Hobart inherited both his bell and his nickname from his father, who was not a native of Thrums. He came from some distant part where the people speak of snecking the door, meaning shut it. In Thrums the word used is steek, and sneck seemed to the inhabitants so droll and ridiculous that Hobart got the name of Snecky. His son left Thrums at the age of ten for the distant farm of Tirl, and did not return until the old bellman's death, twenty years afterwards; but the first remark he overheard on entering the kirkwynd was a conjecture flung across the street by a grey-haired crone, that he would be "little Snecky come to bury auld Snecky."

The father had a reputation in his day for "crying" crimes he was suspected of having committed himself, but the Snecky I knew had too high a sense of his own importance for that. On great occasions, such as the loss of little Davy Dundas, or when a tattie roup had to be cried, he was even offensively inflated; but ordinary announcements, such as the approach of a flying stationer, the roup of a deceased weaver's loom, or the arrival in Thrums of a cart-load of fine "kebec" cheeses, he treated as the merest trifles. I see still the bent legs of the snuffy old man straightening to the tinkle of his bell, and the smirk with which he let the curious populace gather round him. In one hand he ostentatiously displayed the paper on which what he had to cry was written, but, like the minister, he scorned to "read." With the bell carefully tucked under his oxter he gave forth his news in a rasping voice that broke now and again into a squeal. Though Scotch in his unofficial conversation, he was believed to deliver himself on public occasions in the finest English. When trotting from place to place with his news he carried his bell by the tongue as cautiously as if it were a flagon of milk.

Snecky never allowed himself to degenerate into a mere machine. His proclamations were provided by those who employed him, but his soul was his own. Having cried a potato roup he would sometimes add a word of warning, such as, "I wudna advise ye, lads, to hae onything to do wi' thae tatties; they're diseased." Once, just before the cattle market, he was sent round by a local laird to announce that any drover found taking the short cut to the hill through the grounds of Muckle Plowy would be prosecuted to the utmost limits of the law. The people were aghast. "Hoots, lads," Snecky said; "dinna fash yoursels. It's juist a haver o' the grieve's."

One of Hobart's ways of striking terror into evil-doers was to announce, when crying a crime, that he himself knew perfectly well who the culprit was. " I see him brawly," he would say, "standing afore me, an' if he disna instantly mak retribution, I am determined this very day to mak a public example of him."

Before the time of the Burke and Hare murders Snecky's father was sent round Thrums to proclaim the startling news that a grave in the kirkyard had been tampered with. The " resurrectionist" scare was at its height then, and the patriarch, who was one of the men in Thrums paid to watch new graves in the night-time, has often told the story. The town was in a ferment as the news spread, and there were fierce suspicious men among Hobart's hearers who already had the rifler of graves in their eye.

He was a man who worked for the farmers when they required an extra hand, and loafed about the square when they could do without him. No one had a good word for him, and lately he had been flush of money. That was sufficient. There was a rush of angry men through the " pend " that led to his habitation, and he was dragged, panting and terrified, to the kirkyard before he understood what it all meant. To the grave they hurried him, and almost without a word handed him a spade. The whole town gathered round the spot

— a sullen crowd, the women only breaking the silence with their sobs, and the children clinging to their gowns. The suspected resurrectionist understood what was wanted of him, and, flinging off his jacket, began to reopen the grave. Presently the spade struck upon wood, and by and by part of the coffin came in view. That was nothing, for the resurrectionists had a way of breaking the coffin at one end and drawing out the body with tongs. The digger knew this. He broke the boards with the spade and revealed an arm. The people convinced, he dropped the arm savagely, leapt out of the grave and went his way, leaving them to shovel back the earth themselves.

There was humour in the old family as well as in their lodger. I found this out slowly. They used to gather round their peat fire in the evening, after the poultry had gone to sleep on the kitchen rafters, and take off their neighbours. None of them ever laughed; but their neighbours did afford them subject for gossip, and the old man was very sarcastic over other people's old-fashioned ways. When one of the family wanted to go out he did it gradually. He would be sitting "into the fire" browning his corduroy trousers, and he would get up slowly. Then he gazed solemnly before him for a time, and after that, if you watched him narrowly, you would see that he was really moving to the door. Another member of the family took the vacant seat with the same precautions. Will'um, the eldest, has a gun, which customarily stands behind the old eight-day clock; and he takes it with him to the garden to shoot the black-birds. Long before Will'um is ready to let fly, the blackbirds have gone away; and so the gun is never, never fired: but there is a determined look on Will'um's face when he returns from the garden.

In the stormy days of his youth the old man had been a "Black Nib." The Black Nibs were the persons who agitated against the French war; and the public feeling against them ran strong and deep. In Thrums the local Black Nibs were burned in effigy, and whenever they put their heads out of doors they risked being stoned. Even where the authorities were unprejudiced they were helpless to interfere; and as a rule they were as bitter against the Black Nibs as the populace themselves. Once the patriarch was running through the street with a score of the enemy at his heels, and the bailie, opening his window, shouted to them, "Stane the Black Nib oot o' the toon!"

When the patriarch was a young man he was a follower of pleasure. This is the one thing about him that his family have never been able to under-stand. A solemn stroll through the kirkyard was not sufficient relaxation in those riotous times, after a hard day at the loom; and he rarely lost a chance

of going to see a man hanged. There was a good
deal of hanging in those days; and yet the authorities had an ugly way of reprieving condemned
men on whom the sightseers had been counting.
An air of gloom would gather on my old friend's
countenance when he told how he and his contemporaries in Thrums trudged every Saturday for six
weeks to the county town, many miles distant, to
witness the execution of some criminal in whom
they had a local interest, and who, after disappoint-
ing them again and again, was said to have been
bought off by a friend. His crime had been stolen
entrance into a house in Thrums by the chimney,
with intent to rob; and, though this old-fashioned
family did not see it, not the least noticeable incident in the scrimmage that followed was the pru-
dence of the canny housewife. When she saw the
legs coming down the lum, she rushed to the kail-
pot which was on the fire and put on the lid. She
confessed that this was not done to prevent the
visitor's scalding himself, but to save the broth.

The old man was repeated in his three sons.
They told his stories precisely as he did himself,
taking as long in the telling, and making the
points in exactly the same way. By and by they
will come to think that they themselves were of
those past times. Already the young ones look
like contemporaries of their father.

CHAPTER XI

DEVOUT-UNDER-DIFFICULTIES would have been the
name of Lang Tammas had he been of Covenant-
ing times. So I thought one wintry afternoon,
years before I went to the schoolhouse, when he
dropped in to ask the pleasure of my company to
the farmer of Little Rathie's "bural." As a good
Auld Licht, Tammas reserved his swallow-tail coat
and "lum hat" (chimney pot) for the .kirk and
funerals; but the coat would have flapped villain-
ously, to Tammas's eternal ignominy, had he for
one rash moment relaxed his hold on the bottom
button, and it was only by walking sideways, as
horses sometimes try to do, that the hat could be
kept at the angle of decorum. Let it not be
thought that Tammas had asked me to Little
Rathie's funeral on his own responsibility. Burals
were among the few events to break the monotony
of an Auld Licht winter, and invitations were as
much sought after as cards to my lady's dances in
the south. This had been a fair average season
for Tammas, though of his four burials one had

been a bairn's — a mere bagatelle; but had it not been for the death of Little Rathie I would probably not have been out that year at all.

The small farm of Little Rathie lies two miles from Thrums, and Tammas and I trudged manfully through the snow, adding to our numbers as we went. The dress of none differed materially from the precentor's, and the general effect was of septuagenarians in each other's best clothes, though living in low-roofed houses had bent most of them before their time. By a rearrangement of garments, such as making Tammas change coat, hat, and trousers with Cragiebuckle, Silva McQueen, and Sam'l Wilkie respectively, a dexterous tailor might perhaps have supplied each with a "fit." The talk was chiefly of Little Rathie, and sometimes threatened to become animated, when another mourner would fall in and restore the more fitting gloom.

"Ay, ay," the new comer would say, by way of responding to the sober salutation, "Ay, Johnny." Then there was silence, but for the "gluck" with which we lifted our feet from the slush.

"So Little Rathie's been ta'en awa'," Johnny would venture to say, by and by.

"He's gone, Johnny; ay, man, he is so."

"Death must come to all," some one would waken up to murmur.

"Ay," Lang Tammas would reply, putting on

the coping-stone, "in the morning we are strong, and in the evening we are cut down."

"We are so, Tammas; ou ay, we are so; we're here the wan day an' gone the neist."

"Little Rathie wasna a crittur I took till; no, I canna say he was," said Bowie Haggart, so called because his legs described a parabola, "but he maks a very creeditable corp (corpse). I will say that for him. It's wonderfu' hoo death improves a body. Ye cudna hae said as Little Rathie was a weelfaured man when he was i' the flesh."

Bowie was the wright, and attended burials in his official capacity. He had the gift of words to an uncommon degree, and I do not forget his crushing blow at the reputation of the poet Burns, as delivered under the auspices of the Thrums Literary Society. "I am of opeenion," said Bowie, "that the works of Burns is of an immoral tendency. I have not read them myself, but such is my opeenion."

"He was a queer stock, Little Rathie, michty queer," said Tammas Haggart, Bowie's brother, who was a queer stock himself, but was not aware of it; "but, ou, I'm thinkin' the wife had something to do wi't. She was ill to manage, an' Little Rathie hadna the way o' the women. He hadna the knack o' managin' them 's ye micht say — no, Little Rathie hadna the knack."

"They're kittle cattle, the women," said the

farmer of Craigiebuckle — son of the Craigiebuckle
mentioned elsewhere — a little gloomily. "I've
often thocht maiterimony is no onlike the lucky
bags th' auld wifies has at the muckly. There's
prizes an' blanks baith inside, but, losh, ye're far
frae sure what ye'll draw oot when ye put in yer
han'."

"Ou, weel," said Tammas, complacently, "there's
truth in what ye say, but the women can be managed if we have the knack."

"Some o' them," said Cragiebuckle, woefully.

"Ye had yer wark wi' the wife yersel, Tammas,
so ye had," observed Lang Tammas, unbending to
suit his company.

"Ye're speakin' aboot the bit wife's bural," said
Tammas Haggart, with a chuckle, "ay, ay, that
brocht her to reason."

Without much pressure Haggart retold a story
known to the majority of his hearers. He had not
the "knack" of managing women apparently when
he married, for he and his gipsy wife "agreed ill
thegither" at first. Once Chirsty left him and took
up her abode in a house just across the wynd. Instead of routing her out, Tammas, without taking
any one into his confidence, determined to treat
Chirsty as dead, and celebrate her decease in a
"lyke wake" — a last wake. These wakes were
very general in Thrums in the old days, though
they had ceased to be common by the date of

Little Rathie's death. For three days before the
burial the friends and neighbours of the mourners
were invited into the house to partake of food and
drink by the side of the corpse. The dead lay on
chairs covered with a white sheet. Dirges were
sung, and the deceased was extolled, but when
night came the lights were extinguished, and the
corpse was left alone. On the morning of the
funeral tables were spread with a white cloth outside the house, and food and drink were placed
upon them. No neighbour could pass the tables
without paying his respects to the dead; and even
when the house was in a busy, narrow thoroughfare, this part of the ceremony was never omitted.
Tammas did not give Chirsty a wake inside the
house; but one Friday morning — it was market-
day, and the square was consequently full — it
went through the town that the tables were spread
before his door. Young and old collected, wandering round the house, and Tammas stood at the
tables in his blacks inviting every one to eat and
drink. He was pressed to tell what it meant; but
nothing could be got from him except that his
wife was dead. At times he pressed his hands to
his heart, and then he would make wry faces, trying hard to cry. Chirsty watched from a window
across the street, until she perhaps began to fear
that she really was dead. Unable to stand it any
longer, she rushed out into her husband's arms, and

shortly afterwards she could have been seen dismantling the tables.

" She's gone this fower year," Tammas said, when he had finished his story, " but up to the end I had no more trouble wi' Chirsty. No, I had the knack o' her."

" I've heard tell, though," said the sceptical Craigiebuckle, " as Chirsty only cam back to ye because she cudna bear to see the fowk makkin' sae free wi' the whisky."

" I mind hoo she bottled it up at ance, and drove the laddies awa'," said Bowie, " an' I hae seen her after that, Tammas, giein' ye up yer fut an' you no sayin' a word."

" Ou, ay," said the wife-tamer, in the tone of a man who could afford to be generous in trifles, " women maun talk, an' a man hasna aye time to conterdick them, but frae that day I had the knack o' Chirsty."

" Donal Elshioner's was a very seemilar case," broke in Snecky Hobart, shrilly. " Maist o' ye'll mind 'at Donal was michty plague't wi' a drucken wife. Ay, weel, wan day Bowie's man was carryin' a coffin past Donal's door, and Donal an' the wife was there. Says Donal, ' Put doon yer coffin, my man, an' tell's wha it's for.' The laddie rests the coffin on its end, an' says he, ' It's for Davie Fairbrother's guid-wife.' ' Ay, then,' says Donal, ' tak it awa', tak it awa' to Davie, an' tell 'im as ye kin a man wi' a wife 'at wid be glad to neifer (exchange) wi' him.' Man, that terrified Donal's wife ; it did so."

As we delved up the twisting road between two fields, that leads to the farm of Little Rathie, the talk became less general, and another mourner who joined us there was told that the farmer was gone.

" We must all fade as a leaf," said Lang Tammas.

" So we maun, so we maun," admitted the newcomer. " They say," he added, solemnly, " as Little Rathie has left a full teapot."

The reference was to the safe in which the old people in the district stored their gains.

" He was thrifty," said Tammas Haggart, " an' shrewd, too, was Little Rathie. I mind Mr. Dishart admonishin' him for no attendin' a special weather service i' the kirk, when Finny an' Lintool, the twa adjoinin' farmers, baith attendit. ' Ou,' says Little Rathie, ' I thocht to mysel, thinks I, if they get rain for prayin' for't on Finny an' Lintool, we're bound to get the benefit o't on Little Rathie.' "

" Tod," said Snecky, " there's some sense in that ; an' what says the minister ? "

" I d'na kin what he said," admitted Haggart ; " but he took Little Rathie up to the manse, an' if ever I saw a man lookin' sma', it was Little Rathie when he cam oot."

The deceased had left behind him a daughter (herself now known as Little Rathie), quite capa-

ble of attending to the ramshackle "but and ben";
and I remember how she nipped off Tammas's con-
solations to go out and feed the hens. To the
number of about twenty we assembled round the
end of the house to escape the bitter wind, and
here I lost the precentor, who, as an Auld Licht
elder, joined the chief mourners inside. The post
of distinction at a funeral is near the coffin; but it
is not given to every one to be a relative of the
deceased, and there is always much competition
and genteelly concealed disappointment over the
few open vacancies. The window of the room
was decently veiled, but the mourners outside
knew what was happening within, and that it was
not all prayer, neither mourning. A few of the
more reverent uncovered their heads at intervals;
but it would be idle to deny that there was a feeling that Little Rathie's daughter was favouring
Tammas and others somewhat invidiously. Indeed, Robbie Gibruth did not scruple to remark
that she had made "an inauspeecious beginning."
Tammas Haggart, who was melancholy when not
sarcastic, though he brightened up wonderfully at
funerals, reminded Robbie that disappointment is
the lot of man on his earthly pilgrimage; but Haggart knew who were to be invited back after the
burial to the farm, and was inclined to make much
of his position. The secret would doubtless have
been wormed from him had not public attention

been directed into another channel. A prayer was certainly being offered up inside; but the voice was not the voice of the minister.

Lang Tammas told me afterwards that it had seemed at one time "very queistionable" whether Little Rathie would be buried that day at all. The incomprehensible absence of Mr. Dishart (afterwards satisfactorily explained) had raised the unexpected question of the legality of a burial in a case where the minister had not prayed over the "corp." There had even been an indulgence in hot words, and the Reverend Alexander Kewans, a "stickit minister," but not of the Auld Licht persuasion, had withdrawn in dudgeon on hearing Tammas asked to conduct the ceremony instead of himself. But, great as Tammas was on religious questions, a pillar of the Auld Licht kirk, the Shorter Catechism at his finger-ends, a sad want of words at the very time when he needed them most, incapacitated him for prayer in public, and it was providential that Bowie proved himself a man of parts. But Tammas tells me that the wright grossly abused his position, by praying at such length that Craigiebuckle fell asleep, and the mistress had to rise and hang the pot on the fire higher up the joist, lest its contents should burn before the return from the funeral. Loury grew the sky, and more and more anxious the face of Little Rathie's daughter, and still Bowie prayed on. Had it not been for the impatience of the precentor and the grumbling of the mourners outside, there is no saying when the remains would have been lifted through the " bole," or little window.

Hearses had hardly come in at this time and the coffin was carried by the mourners on long stakes. The straggling procession of pedestrians behind wound its slow way in the waning light to the kirkyard, showing startlingly black against the dazzling snow; and it was not until the earth rattled on the coffin-lid that Little Rathie's nearest male relative seemed to remember his last mournful duty to the dead. Sidling up to the favoured mourners, he remarked casually and in the most emotionless tone he could assume: " They're expec'in ye to stap doon the length o' Little Rathie noo. Aye, aye, he's gone. Na, na, nae refoosal, Da-avit; ye was aye a guid friend till him, an' it's onything a body can do for him noo."

Though the uninvited slunk away sorrowfully, the entertainment provided at Auld Licht houses of mourning was characteristic of a stern and sober sect. They got to eat and to drink to the extent, as a rule, of a " lippy " of shortbread and a " brew " of toddy; but open Bibles lay on the table, and the eyes of each were on his neighbours to catch them transgressing, and offer up a prayer for them on the spot. Ay me! there is no Bowie nowadays to fill an absent minister's shoes.

CHAPTER XII

THE ministers in the town did not hold with literature. When the most notorious of the clubs met in the town-house under the presidentship of Gavin Ogilvy, who was no better than a poacher, and was troubled in his mind because writers called Pope a poet, there was frequently a wrangle over the question, Is literature necessarily immoral? It was a fighting club, and on Friday nights the few respectable, god-fearing members dandered to the town-house, as if merely curious to have another look at the building. If Lang Tammas, who was dead against letters, was in sight they wandered off, but when there were no spies abroad they slunk up the stair. The attendance was greatest on dark nights, though Gavin himself and some other characters would have marched straight to the meeting in broad daylight. Tammas Haggart, who did not think much of Milton's devil, had married a gypsy woman for an experiment, and the Coat of Many Colours did not know where his wife was. As a rule, however, the members were wild bachelors. When they married they had to settle down.

Gavin's essay on Will'um Pitt, the Father of the Taxes, led to the club's being bundled out of the town-house, where people said it should never have been allowed to meet. There was a terrible town when Tammas Haggart then disclosed the secret of Mr. Byars's supposed approval of the club. Mr. Byars was the Auld Licht minister whom Mr. Dishart succeeded, and it was well known that he had advised the authorities to grant the use of the little town-house to the club on Friday evenings. As he solemnly warned his congregation against attending the meetings the position he had taken up created talk, and Lang Tammas called at the manse with Sanders Whamond to remonstrate. The minister, however, harangued them on their sinfulness in daring to question the like of him, and they had to retire vanquished though dissatisfied. Then came the disclosures of Tammas Haggart, who was never properly secured by the Auld Lichts until Mr. Dishart took him in hand. It was Tammas who wrote anonymous letters to Mr. Byars about the scarlet woman, and, strange to say, this led to the club's being allowed to meet in the town-house. The minister, after many days, discovered who his correspondent was, and succeeded in inveigling the stone-breaker to the manse. There, with the door snibbed, he opened out on Tammas, who, after his usual manner when hard pressed, pretended to be deaf. This sudden fit of deafness so exasperated the minister that he flung a book at Tammas. The scene that followed was one that few Auld Licht manses can have witnessed. According to Tammas the book had hardly reached the floor when the minister turned white. Tammas picked up the missile. It was a Bible. The two men looked at each other. Beneath the window Mr. Byars's children were prattling. His wife was moving about in the next room, little thinking what had happened. The minister held out his hand for the Bible, but Tammas shook his head, and then Mr. Byars shrank into a chair. Finally, it was arranged that if Tammas kept the affair to himself the minister would say a good word to the Bailie about the literary club. After that the stone-breaker used to go from house to house, twisting his mouth to the side and remarking that he could tell such a tale of Mr. Byars as would lead to a split in the kirk. When the town-house was locked on the club Tammas spoke out, but though the scandal ran from door to door, as I have seen a pig in a fluster do, the minister did not lose his place. Tammas preserved the Bible, and showed it complacently to visitors as the present he got from Mr. Byars. The minister knew this, and it turned his temper

sour. Tammas's proud moments, after that, were
when he passed the minister.

Driven from the town-house, literature found a
table with forms round it in a tavern hard by,
where the club, lopped of its most respectable
members, kept the blinds down and talked openly
of Shakspeare. It was a low-roofed room, with
pieces of lime hanging from the ceiling and peel-
ing walls. The floor had a slope that tended to
fling the debater forward, and its boards, lying
loose on an uneven foundation, rose and looked at
you as you crossed the room. In winter, when the
meetings were held regularly every fortnight, a fire
of peat, sod, and dross lit up the curious company
who sat round the table shaking their heads over
Shelley's mysticism, or requiring to be called to
order because they would not wait their turn to
deny an essayist's assertion that Berkeley's style
was superior to David Hume's. Davit Hume,
they said, and Watty Scott. Burns was simply
referred to as Rob or Robbie.

There was little drinking at these meetings, for
the members knew what they were talking about,
and your mind had to gallop to keep up with the
flow of reasoning. Thrums is rather a remarkable
town. There are scores and scores of houses in it
that have sent their sons to college (by what a
struggle!), some to make their way to the front in
their professions, and others, perhaps, despite their

broadcloth, never to be a patch on their parents. In that literary club there were men of a reading so wide and catholic that it might put some graduates of the universities to shame, and of an intellect so keen that had it not had a crook in it their fame would have crossed the county. Most of them had but a thread-bare existence, for you weave slowly with a Wordsworth open before you, and some were strange Bohemians (which does not do in Thrums), yet others wandered into the world and compelled it to recognize them. There is a London barrister whose father belonged to the club. Not many years ago a man died on the staff of the *Times*, who, when he was a weaver near Thrums, was one of the club's prominent members. He taught himself shorthand by the light of a cruizey, and got a post on a Perth paper, afterwards on the *Scotsman* and the *Witness*, and finally on the *Times*. Several other men of his type had a history worth reading, but it is not for me to write. Yet I may say that there is still at least one of the original members of the club left behind in Thrums to whom some of the literary dandies might lift their hats.

Gavin Ogilvy I only knew as a weaver and a poacher; a lank, long-armed man, much bent from crouching in ditches whence he watched his snares. To the young he was a romantic figure, because they saw him frequently in the fields with his call-birds tempting siskins, yellow yites, and linties to twigs which he had previously smeared with lime. He made the lime from the tough roots of holly; sometimes from linseed oil, which is boiled until thick, when it is taken out of the pot and drawn and stretched with the hands like elastic. Gavin was also a famous hare-snarer at a time when the ploughman looked upon this form of poaching as his perquisite. The snare was of wire, so constructed that the hare entangled itself the more when trying to escape, and it was placed across the little roads through the fields to which hares confine themselves, with a heavy stone attached to it by a string. Once Gavin caught a toad (fox) instead of a hare, and did not discover his mistake until it had him by the teeth. He was not able to weave for two months. The grouse-netting was more lucrative and more exciting, and women engaged in it with their husbands. It is told of Gavin that he was on one occasion chased by a gamekeeper over moor and hill for twenty miles, and that by and by when the one sank down exhausted so did the other. They would sit fifty yards apart, glaring at each other. The poacher eventually escaped. This, curious as it may seem, is the man whose eloquence at the club has not been forgotten in fifty years. "Thus did he stand," I have been told recently, "exclaiming in language sublime that the soul shall bloom in immortal youth through the ruin and wrack of time."

Another member read to the club an account of his journey to Lochnagar, which was afterwards published in *Chambers's Journal*. He was celebrated for his descriptions of scenery, and was not the only member of the club whose essays got into print. More memorable perhaps was an itinerant match-seller known to Thrums and the surrounding towns as the literary spunk-seller. He was a wizened, shivering old man, often barefooted, wearing at the best a thin ragged coat that had been black but was green-brown with age, and he made his spunks as well as sold them. He brought Bacon and Adam Smith into Thrums, and he loved to recite long screeds from Spenser, with a running commentary on the versification and the luxuriance of the diction. Of Jamie's death I do not care to write. He went without many a dinner in order to buy a book.

The Coat of Many Colours and Silva Robbie were two street preachers who gave the Thrums ministers some work. They occasionally appeared at the club. The Coat of Many Colours was so called because he wore a garment consisting of patches of cloth of various colours sewed together. It hung down to his heels. He may have been cracked rather than inspired, but he was a power in the square where he preached, the women de-

claring that he was gifted by God. An awe filled
even the men, when he admonished them for using strong language, for at such a time he would
remind them of the woe which fell upon Tibbie
Mason. Tibbie had been notorious in her day for
evil-speaking, especially for her free use of the
word handless, which she flung a hundred times
in a week at her man, and even at her old mother.
Her punishment was to have a son born without
hands. The Coat of Many Colours also told of
the liar who exclaimed, "If this is not gospel
true may I stand here for ever," and who is standing on that spot still, only nobody knows where
it is. George Wishart was the Coat's hero, and
often he has told in the Square how Wishart saved
Dundee. It was the time when the plague lay
over Scotland, and in Dundee they saw it approaching from the West in the form of a great
black cloud. They fell on their knees and prayed,
crying to the cloud to pass them by, and while
they prayed it came nearer. Then they looked
around for the most holy man among them, to in-
tervene with God on their behalf. All eyes turned
to George Wishart, and he stood up, stretching
his arms to the cloud and prayed, and it rolled
back. Thus Dundee was saved from the plague,
but when Wishart ended his prayer he was alone,
for the people had all returned to their homes.
Less of a genuine man than the Coat of Many

Colours was Silva Robbie, who had horrid fits of laughing in the middle of his prayers, and even fell in a paroxysm of laughter from the chair on which he stood. In the club he said things not to be borne, though logical up to a certain point.

Tammas Haggart was the most sarcastic member of the club, being celebrated for his sarcasm far and wide. It was a remarkable thing about him, often spoken of, that if you went to Tammas with a stranger and asked him to say a sarcastic thing that the man might take away as a specimen, he could not do it. "Na, na," Tammas would say, after a few trials, referring to sarcasm, "she's no a critter to force. Ye maun lat her tak her ain time. Sometimes she's dry like the pump, an' syne, again, oot she comes in a gush." The most sarcastic thing the stone-breaker ever said was frequently marvelled over in Thrums, both before and behind his face, but unfortunately no one could ever remember what it was. The subject, however, was Cha Tamson's potato pit. There is little doubt that it was a fit of sarcasm that induced Tammas to marry a gypsy lassie. Mr. Byars would not join them, so Tammas had himself married by Jimmy Pawse, the gay little gypsy king, and after that the minister re-married them. The marriage over the tongs is a thing to scandalise any well-brought-up person, for before he joined the couple's hands, Jimmy jumped about

in a startling way, uttering wild gibberish, and
after the ceremony was over there was rough work,
with incantations and blowing on pipes. Tammas
always held that this marriage turned out better
than he had expected, though he had his trials like
other married men. Among them was Chirsty's
way of climbing on to the dresser to get at the
higher part of the plate-rack. One evening I
called in to have a smoke with the stone-breaker,
and while we were talking Chirsty climbed the
dresser. The next moment she was on the floor
on her back, wailing, but Tammas smoked on
imperturbably. "Do you not see what has happened, man?" I cried. "Ou," said Tammas,
"she's aye fa'in aff the dresser."

Of the schoolmasters who were at times members of the club, Mr. Dickie was the ripest scholar,
but my predecessor at the school-house had a way
of sneering at him that was as good as sarcasm.
When they were on their legs at the same time,
asking each other passionately to be calm, and rolling out lines from Homer, that made the inn-
keeper look fearfully to the fastenings of the door,
their heads very nearly came together although the
table was between them. The old dominie had an
advantage in being the shorter man, for he could
hammer on the table as he spoke, while gaunt Mr.
Dickie had to stoop to it. Mr. McRittie's argu-
ments were a series of nails that he knocked into

the table, and he did it in a workmanlike manner. Mr. Dickie, though he kept firm on his feet, swayed his body until by and by his head was rotating in a large circle. The mathematical figure he made was a cone revolving on its apex. Gavin's reinstalment in the chair year after year was made by the disappointed dominie the subject of some tart verses which he called an epode, but Gavin crushed him when they were read before the club. "Satire," he said, "is a legitimate weapon, used with michty effect by Swift, Sammy Butler, and others, and I dount object to being made the subject of creeticism. It has often been called a t'nife (knife), but them as is not used to t'nives cuts their hands, and ye'll a' observe that Mr. McRittie's fingers is bleedin'." All eyes were turned upon the dominie's hand, and though he pocketed it smartly several members had seen the blood. The dominie was a rare visitor at the club after that, though he outlived poor Mr. Dickie by many years. Mr. Dickie was a teacher in Tilliedrum, but he was ruined by drink. He wandered from town to town, reciting Greek and Latin poetry to any one who would give him a dram, and sometimes he wept and moaned aloud in the street, crying, "Poor Mr. Dickie! poor Mr. Dickie!"

The leading poet in a club of poets was Dite Walls, who kept a school when there were scholars, and weaved when there were none. He had a song that was published in a half-penny leaflet about the famous lawsuit instituted by the farmer of Teuchbusses against the Laird of Drumlee. The laird was alleged to have taken from the land of Teuchbusses sufficient broom to make a besom thereof, and I am not certain that the case is settled to this day. It was Dite or another member of the club who wrote, "The Wife o' Deeside," of all the songs of the period the one that had the greatest vogue in the county at a time when Lord Jeffrey was cursed at every fireside in Thrums. The wife of Deeside was tried for the murder of her servant who had infatuated the young laird, and had it not been that Jeffrey defended her she would, in the words of the song, have "hung like a troot." It is not easy now to conceive the rage against Jeffrey when the woman was acquitted. The song was sung and recited in the streets, at the smiddy, in bothies, and by firesides, to the shaking of fists and the grinding of teeth. It began —

> " Ye'll a' hae hear tell o' the wife o' Deeside,
> Ye'll a' hae hear tell o' the wife o' Deeside,
> She poisoned her maid for to keep up her pride,
> Ye'll a' hae hear tell o' the wife o' Deeside."

Before the excitement had abated, Jeffrey was in Tilliedrum for electioneering purposes, and he was mobbed in the streets. Angry crowds pressed close to howl, " Wife o' Deeside ! " at him. A contingent from Thrums was there, and it was long afterwards told of Sam'l Todd, by himself, that he hit Jeffrey on the back of the head with a clod of earth.

Johnny McQuhatty, a brother of the T'nowhead farmer, was the one taciturn member of the club, and you had only to look at him to know that he had a secret. He was a great genius at the hand-loom, and invented a loom for the weaving of linen such as has not been seen before or since. In the day-time he kept guard over his " shop," into which no one was allowed to enter, and the fame of his loom was so great that he had to watch over it with a gun. At night he weaved, and when the result at last pleased him he made the linen into shirts, all of which he stitched together with his own hands, even to the buttonholes. He sent one shirt to the Queen, and another to the Duchess of Athole, mentioning a very large price for them, which he got. Then he destroyed his wonderful loom, and how it was made no one will ever know. Johnny only took to literature after he had made his name, and he seldom spoke at the club except when ghosts and the like were the subject of de-bate, as they tended to be when the farmer of Muckle Haws could get in a word. Muckle Haws was fascinated by Johnny's sneers at super-stition, and sometimes on dark nights the inventor had to make his courage good by seeing the far-

mer past the doulie yates (ghost gates), which
Muckle Haws had to go perilously near on his
way home. Johnny was a small man, but it was
the burly farmer who shook at sight of the gates
standing out white in the night. White gates have
an evil name still, and Muckle Haws was full of
horrors as he drew near them, clinging to Johnny's
arm. It was on such a night, he would remember,
that he saw the White Lady go through the gates
greeting sorely, with a dead bairn in her arms,
while water kelpies laughed and splashed in the
pools, and the witches danced in a ring round
Broken Buss. That very night twelve months
ago the packman was murdered at Broken Buss,
and Easie Pettie hanged herself on the stump of a
tree. Last night there were ugly sounds from the
quarry of Croup, where the bairn lies buried, and
it's not mous (canny) to be out at such a time.
The farmer had seen spectre maidens walking
round the ruined castle of Darg, and the castle all
lit up with flaring torches, and dead knights and
ladies sitting in the halls at the wine-cup, and the
devil himself flapping his wings on the ramparts.

When the debates were political, two members
with the gift of song fired the blood with their own
poems about taxation and the depopulation of the
Highlands, and by selling these songs from door
to door they made their livelihood.

Books and pamphlets were brought into the

town by the flying stationers, as they were called,
who visited the square periodically carrying their
wares on their backs, except at the Muckly, when
they had their stall and even sold books by auction.
The flying stationer best known to Thrums was
Sandersy Riach, who was stricken from head to
foot with the palsy, and could only speak with a
quaver in consequence. Sandersy brought to the
members of the club all the great books he could
get second hand, but his stock-in-trade was
Thrummy Cap and Akenstaff, the Fishwives of
Buckhaven, the Devil upon Two Sticks, Gilderoy,
Sir James the Rose, the Brownie of Badenoch, the
Ghaist of Firenden, and the like. It was from
Sandersy that Tammas Haggart bought his copy
of Shakspeare, whom Mr. Dishart could never
abide. Tammas kept what he had done from his
wife, but Chirsty saw a deterioration setting in and
told the minister of her suspicions. Mr. Dishart
was newly placed at the time and very vigorous,
and the way he shook the truth out of Tammas
was grand. The minister pulled Tammas the one
way and Gavin pulled him the other, but Mr.
Dishart was not the man to be beaten, and he landed
Tammas in the Auld Licht kirk before the year
was out. Chirsty buried Shakspeare in the yard.

BETTER DEAD

CHAPTER I

WHEN Andrew Riach went to London, his intention was to become private secretary to a member of the Cabinet. If time permitted, he proposed writing for the Press.

"It might be better if you and Clarrie understood each other," the minister said.

It was their last night together. They faced each other in the manse-parlour at Wheens, whose low, peeled ceiling had threatened Mr. Eassie at his desk every time he looked up with his pen in his mouth until his wife died, when he ceased to notice things. The one picture on the walls, an engraving of a boy in velveteen, astride a tree, entitled "Boyhood of Bunyan," had started life with him. The horsehair chairs were not torn, and you did not require to know the sofa before you sat down on it, that day thirty years before, when a chubby minister and his lady walked to the manse between two cart-loads of furniture, trying not to look elated.

Clarrie rose to go, when she heard her name. The love-light was in her eyes, but Andrew did

not open the door for her, for he was a Scotch
graduate. Besides, she might one day be his
wife.

The minister's toddy-ladle clinked against his
tumbler, but Andrew did not speak. Clarrie was
the girl he generally adored.

" As for Clarrie," he said at last, " she puts me
in an awkward position. How do I know that I
love her ? "

" You have known each other a long time," said
the minister.

His guest was cleaning his pipe with a hair-pin,
that his quick eye had detected on the carpet.

" And she is devoted to you," continued Mr.
Eassie.

The young man nodded.

" What I fear," he said, " is that we have known
each other too long. Perhaps my feeling for Clarrie is only brotherly—"

" Hers for you, Andrew, is more than sisterly."

" Admitted. But consider, Mr. Eassie, she has
only seen the world in soirées. Every girl has her
day-dreams, and Clarrie has perhaps made a dream
of me. She is impulsive, given to idealisation,
and hopelessly illogical."

The minister moved uneasily in his chair.

" I have reasoned out her present relation to
me," the young man went on, " and, the more you
reduce it to the usual formulæ, the more illogical

192

it becomes. Clarrie could possibly describe me, but define me — never. What is our prospect of happiness in these circumstances ? "

" But love—" began Mr. Eassie.

" Love ! " exclaimed Andrew. " Is there such a thing ? Reduce it to syllogistic form, and how does it look in Barbara ? "

For the moment there was almost some expression in his face, and he suffered from a determination of words to the mouth.

" Love and logic," Mr. Eassie interposed, " are hardly kindred studies."

" Is love a study at all ? " asked Andrew, bitterly. " It is but the trail of idleness. But all idleness is folly; therefore, love is folly."

Mr. Eassie was not so keen a logician as his guest, but he had age for a major premiss. He was easy-going rather than a coward; a preacher who, in the pulpit, looked difficulties genially in the face, and passed them by.

Riach had a very long neck. He was twenty-five years of age, fair, and somewhat heavily built, with a face as inexpressive as book-covers.

A native of Wheens and an orphan, he had been brought up by his uncle, who was a weaver and read Herodotus in the original. The uncle starved himself to buy books and talk about them, until one day he got a good meal, and died of it. Then Andrew apprenticed himself to a tailor.

When his time was out, he walked fifty miles to Aberdeen University, and got a bursary. He had been there a month, when his professor said good-naturedly —

"Don't you think, Mr. Riach, you would get on better if you took your hands out of your pockets?"

"No, sir, I don't think so," replied Andrew, in all honesty.

When told that he must apologise, he did not see it, but was willing to argue the matter out.

Next year he matriculated at Edinburgh, sharing one room with two others; studying through the night, and getting their bed when they rose. He was a failure in the classics, because they left you where you were, but in his third year he woke the logic class-room, and frightened the professor of moral philosophy.

He was nearly rusticated for praying at a debating society for a divinity professor who was in the chair.

"O Lord!" he cried, fervently, "open his eyes, guide his tottering footsteps, and lead him from the paths of folly into those that are lovely and of good report, for lo! his days are numbered, and the sickle has been sharpened, and the corn is not yet ripe for the cutting."

When Andrew graduated he was known as a student of mark.

He returned to Wheens, before setting out for London, with the consciousness of his worth.

Yet he was only born to follow, and his chance of making a noise in the world rested on his meeting a stronger than himself. During his summer vacations he had weaved sufficient money to keep himself during the winter on porridge and potatoes.

Clarrie was beautiful and all that.

" We'll say no more about it, then," the minister said after a pause.

" The matter," replied Andrew, "cannot be dismissed in that way. Reasonable or not, I do undoubtedly experience sensations similar to Clarrie's. But in my love I notice a distinct ebb and flow. There are times when I don't care a hang for her."

" Andrew ! "

" I beg your pardon. Still, it is you who have insisted on discussing this question in the particular instance. Love in the abstract is of much greater moment."

" I have sometimes thought, Andrew," Mr. Eassie said, "that you are lacking in the imaginative faculty."

" In other words, love is a mere fancy. Grant that, and see to what it leads. By imagining that I have Clarrie with me I am as well off as if I really had. Why, then, should I go to needless expense, and take her from you ? "

The white-haired minister rose, for the ten o'clock bell was ringing and it was time for family worship.

"My boy," he said, "if there must be a sacrifice let the old man make it. I, too, have imagination."

For the moment there was a majesty about him that was foreign to his usual bearing. Andrew was touched, and gripped his hand.

"Rather," he cried, "let the girl we both love remain with you. She will be here waiting for me — should I return."

"More likely," said the minister, "she will be at the bank."

The banker was unmarried, and had once in February and again in June seen Clarrie home from the Dorcas Society. The town talked about it. Strictly speaking, gentlemen should not attend these meetings; but in Wheens there was not much difference between the men and the women.

That night, as Clarrie bade Andrew farewell at the garden gate, he took her head in his hands and asked what this talk about the banker meant.

It was no ignoble curiosity that prompted him. He would rather have got engaged to her there and then than have left without feeling sure of her.

His sweetheart looked her reply straight into his eyes.

" Andrew ! " was all she said.

It was sufficient.   He knew that he did not require to press his point.

Lover's watches stand still.   At last Andrew
stooped and kissed her upturned face.

" If a herring and a half," he said anxiously,
" cost three half-pence, how many will you get for
elevenpence ? "

Clarrie was mute.

Andrew shuddered ; he felt that he was making
a mistake.

" Why do I kiss you ? " he cried.   " What good
does it do either of us ? "

He looked fiercely at his companion, and her
eyes filled with tears.

" Where even is the pleasure in it ? " he added
brutally.

The only objectionable thing about Clarrie was
her long hair.

She wore a black frock and looked very break-
able.   Nothing irritates a man so much.

Andrew gathered her passionately in his arms,
while a pained, puzzled expression struggled to
reach his face.

Then he replaced her roughly on the ground
and left her.

It was impossible to say whether they were engaged.

CHAPTER II

ANDREW reached King's Cross on the following Wednesday morning.

It was the first time he had set foot in England, and he naturally thought of Bannockburn.

He left his box in the cloak-room, and, finding his way into Bloomsbury, took a bed-room at the top of a house in Bernard Street.

Then he returned for his box, carried it on his back to his lodgings, and went out to buy a straw hat. It had not struck him to be lonely.

He bought two pork pies in an eating-house in Gray's Inn Road, and set out for Harley Street, looking at London on the way.

Mr. Gladstone was at home, but all his private secretaryships were already filled.

Andrew was not greatly disappointed, though he was too polite to say so. In politics he was a granite-headed Radical; and on several questions, such as the Church and Free Education, the two men were hopelessly at variance.

Mr. Chamberlain was the man with whom, on the whole, he believed it would be best to work. But Mr. Chamberlain could not even see him.

Looking back to this time, it is impossible not to speculate upon how things might have turned out had the Radical party taken Andrew to them in his day of devotion to their cause.

This is the saddest spectacle in life, a brave young man's first meeting with the world. How rapidly the milk turns to gall! For the cruellest of his acts the vivisectionist has not even the excuse that science benefits.

Here was a young Scotchman, able, pure, of noble ambition, and a first medallist in metaphysics. Genius was written on his brow. He may have written it himself, but it was there.

He offered to take a pound a week less than any other secretary in London. Not a Cabinet Minister would have him. Lord Randolph Churchill would not speak to him. He had fifty-eight testimonials with him. They would neither read nor listen to them.

He could not fasten a quarrel on London, for it never recognised his existence. What a commentary on our vaunted political life!

Andrew tried the Press.

He sent one of the finest things that was ever written on the Ontology of Being to paper after paper, and it was never used. He threatened the

"Times" with legal proceedings if it did not return the manuscript.

The "Standard" sent him somebody else's manuscript, and seemed to think it would do as well.

In a fortnight his enthusiasm had been bled to death.

His testimonials were his comfort and his curse. He would have committed suicide without them, but they kept him out of situations.

He had the fifty-eight by heart, and went over them to himself all day. He fell asleep with them, and they were there when he woke.

The moment he found himself in a great man's presence he began:

"From the Rev. Peter Mackay, D.D., author of 'The Disruption Divines,' Minister of Free St. King's, Dundee.—I have much pleasure in stating that I have known Mr. Andrew Gordon Cummings Riach for many years, and have been led to form a high opinion of his ability. In the summer of 18— Mr. Riach had entire charge of a class in my Sabbath school, when I had ample opportunity of testing his efficiency, unwearying patience, exceptional power of illustration and high Christian character," and so on.

Or he might begin at the beginning:

"Testimonials in favour of Andrew G. C. Riach, M. A. (Edin.), applicant for the post of Private Secretary to any one of her Majesty's Cabinet Min-

isters, 6 Candlish Street, Wheens, N. B.— I, Andrew G. C. Riach, beg to offer myself as a candi-
date for the post of private secretary, and submit
the following testimonials in my favour for your
consideration. I am twenty-five years of age, a
Master of Arts of the University of Edinburgh,
and a member of the Free Church of Scotland.
At the University I succeeded in carrying a bursary of 14*l.* 10*s.* per annum, tenable for four years.
I was first medallist in the class of Logic and Metaphysics, thirteenth prizeman in Mathematics, and
had a certificate of merit in the class of Natural
Philosophy, as will be seen from my testimonials."

However, he seldom got as far as this.

It was when alone that these testimonials were
his truest solace. Had you met him in the Strand
conning them over, you might have taken him for
an actor. He had a yearning to stop strangers in
the streets and try a testimonial's effect on them.

Every young man is not equally unfortunate.

Riach's appearance was against him.

There was a suggestion of latent strength about
him that made strangers uncomfortable. Even
the friends who thought they understood him
liked him to go away.

Lord Rosebery made several jokes to him, and
Andrew only looked at him in response. The
general feeling was that he was sneering at you
somewhere in his inside.

BETTER DEAD

Let us do no one an injustice.

As it turned out, the Cabinet and Press were but being used in this case as the means to an end.

A grand work lay ready for Andrew's hand when he was fit to perform it, but he had to learn Naked Truth first. It was ordained that they should teach it him. Providence sometimes makes use of strange instruments.

Riach had two pounds with him when he came to London, and in a month they had almost gone.

Now and again he made an odd five shillings.

Do you know how men in his position live in London?

He could not afford the profession of not having any.

At one time he was a phrasemonger for politicians, especially for the Irish members, who were the only ones that paid.

Some of his phrases have become Parliamentary. Thus "Buckshot" was his. "Mend them — End them," "Grand Old Man," and "Legislation by Picnic" may all be traced to the struggling young man from Wheens.*

He supplied the material for obituary notices.

When the newspaper placards announced the

---

* Some time afterwards Lord Rosebery convulsed an audience by a story about a friend of his who complained that you get "no forrarder" on claret. Andrew was that friend.

serious illness of a distinguished man, he made up characteristic anecdotes about his childhood, his reputation at school, his first love, and sent them as the reminiscences of a friend to the great London dailies. These were the only things of his they used. As often as not the invalid got better, and then Andrew went without a dinner.

Once he offered his services to a Conservative statesman; at another time he shot himself in the coat in Northumberland Street, Strand, to oblige an evening paper (five shillings).

He fainted in the pit of a theatre to the bribe of an emotional tragedian (a guinea).

He assaulted a young lady and her aunt with a view to robbery, in a quiet thoroughfare, by arrangement with a young gentleman, who rescued them and made him run (ten shillings).

It got into the papers that he had fled from the wax policeman at Tussaud's (half-a-crown).

More than once he sold his body in advance to the doctors, and was never able to buy it out.*

It would be a labour, thankless as impossible, to recover now all the devices by which Andrew disgraced his manhood during these weeks rather than die. As well count the "drinks" an actor has in a day.

* He had fine ideas, but no money to work them out. One was to start a serious "Spectator," on the lines of the present one, but not so flippant and frivolous.

BETTER DEAD

It is not our part to climb down into the depths after him. He re-appeared eventually, or this record would never have been written.

During this period of gloom, Clarrie wrote him frequently long and tender epistles.

More strictly, the minister wrote them, for he had the gift of beautiful sentiment in letters, which had been denied to her.

She copied them, however, and signed them, and they were a great consolation.

The love of a good girl is a priceless possession, or rather, in this case, of a good minister.

So long as you do not know which, it does not make much difference.

At times Andrew's reason may have been unhinged, less on account of his reverses than because no one spoke to him.

There were days and nights when he rushed all over London.

In the principal streets the stolid-faced Scotchman in a straw hat became a familiar figure.

Strange fancies held him. He stood for an hour at a time looking at his face in a shop-window.

The boot-blacks pointed at him and he disappeared down passages.

He shook his fist at the 'bus-conductors, who would not leave him alone.

In the yellow night policemen drew back scared, as he hurried past them on his way to nowhere.

In the day-time Oxford Street was his favourite thoroughfare. He was very irritable at this time, and could not leave his fellow wayfarers alone.

More than once he poked his walking-stick through the eyeglass of a brave young gentleman.

He would turn swiftly round to catch people looking at him.

When a small boy came in his way, he took him by the neck and planted him on the curb-stone.

If a man approached simpering, Andrew stopped and gazed at him. The smile went from the stranger's face; he blushed or looked fierce. When he turned round, Andrew still had his eye on him. Sometimes he came bouncing back.

" What are you so confoundedly happy about ? " Andrew asked.

When he found a crowd gazing in at a "while you wait" shop-window, or entranced over the paving of a street —

"Splendid, isn't it ? " he said to the person nearest him.

He dropped a penny, which he could ill spare, into the hat of an exquisite who annoyed him by his way of lifting it to a lady.

When he saw a man crossing the street too daintily, he ran after him and hit him over the legs.

Even on his worst days his reasoning powers

never left him. Once a mother let her child slip from her arms to the pavement.

She gave a shriek.

"My good woman," said Andrew, testily, "what difference can one infant in the world more or less make?"

We come now to an eccentricity, engendered of loneliness, that altered the whole course of his life. Want had battered down his door. Truth had been evolved from despair. He was at last to have a flash into salvation.

To give an object to his walks abroad he would fasten upon a wayfarer and follow him till he ran him to his destination. Chance led to his selecting one quarry rather than another. He would dog a man's footsteps, struck by the glossiness of his boots, or to discover what he was in such a hurry about, or merely because he had a good back to follow. Probably he seldom knew what attracted him, and sometimes when he realised the pursuit he gave it up.

On these occasions there was one person only who really interested him. This was a man, somewhat over middle age, of singularly noble and distinguished bearing. His brow was furrowed with lines, but they spoke of cares of the past. Benevolence had settled on his face. It was as if, after a weary struggle, the sun had broken through the heavy clouds. He was attired in the ordinary

206

dress of an English gentleman; but once, when he raised his head to see if it rained, Andrew noticed that he only wore a woollen shirt, without a necktie. As a rule, his well-trimmed, venerable beard hid this from view.

He seemed a man of unostentatious means. Andrew lost him in Drury Lane and found him again in Piccadilly. He was generally alone, never twice with the same person. His business was scattered, or it was his pleasure that kept him busy. He struck the observer as always being on the outlook for someone who did not come.

Why attempt to account for the nameless fascination he exercised over the young Scotchman? We speak lightly of mesmeric influence, but, after all, there is only one mesmerist for youth — a good woman or a good man. Depend upon it, that is why so many "mesmerists" have mistaken their vocation. Andrew took to prowling about the streets looking for this man, like a dog that has lost its master.

The day came when they met.

Andrew was returning from the Crystal Palace, which he had been viewing from the outside. He had walked both ways. Just as he rounded the upper end of Chancery Lane, a man walking rapidly struck against him, whirled him aside, and hurried on.

The day was done, but as yet the lamps only dimmed the streets.

Andrew had been dreaming, and the jerk woke him to the roar of London.

It was as if he had taken his fingers from his ears.

He staggered, dazed, against a 'bus-horse, but the next moment he was in pursuit of the stranger. It was but a continuation of his dream. He felt that something was about to happen. He had never seen this man disturbed before.

Chancery Lane swarmed with lawyers, but if they had not made way Andrew would have walked over them.

He clove his way between those walking abreast, and struck down an arm extended to point out the Law Courts. When he neared the stranger, he slightly slackened his pace, but it was a stampede even then.

Suddenly the pursued came to a dead stop and gazed for twenty minutes in at a pastry-cook's window. Andrew waited for him. Then they started off again, much more leisurely.

They turned Chancery Lane almost together. All this time Andrew had failed to catch sight of the other's face.

He stopped twice in the Strand for a few minutes.

At Charing Cross he seemed for a moment at a loss. Then he sprang across the street, and went back the way he came.

BETTER DEAD

It was now for the first time that a strange notion illumined Andrew's brain. It bewildered him,
and left him in darkness the next moment. But
his blood was running hot now, and his eyes were
glassy.

They turned down Arundel Street.

It was getting dark. There were not a dozen
people in the narrow thoroughfare.

His former thought leapt back into Andrew's
mind — not a fancy now, but a fact. The stranger
was following someone too.

For what purpose ? His own ?

Andrew did not put the question to himself.

There were not twenty yards between the three
of them.

What Riach saw in front was a short stout man
proceeding cheerfully down the street. He delayed in a doorway to light a cigar, and the
stranger stopped as if turned to stone.

Andrew stopped too.

They were like the wheels of a watch. The
first wheel moved on, and set the others going
again.

For a hundred yards or more they walked in
procession in a westerly direction without meeting a
human being. At last the first of the trio half turned
on his heel and leant over the Embankment.

Riach drew back into the shade, just before the
stranger took a lightning glance behind him.

The young man saw his face now. It was never fuller of noble purpose; yet why did Andrew cry out?

The next moment the stranger had darted forward, slipped his arms round the little man's legs, and toppled him into the river.

There was a splash but no shriek.

Andrew bounded forward, but the stranger held him by one hand. His clear blue eyes looked down a little wistfully upon the young Scotchman, who never felt the fascination of a master-mind more than at that moment. As if feeling his power, the elder man relaxed his hold and pointed to the spot where his victim had disappeared.

"He was a good man," he said, more to himself than to Andrew, "and the world has lost a great philanthropist; but he is better as he is."

Then he lifted a paving-stone, and peered long and earnestly into the waters.

The short stout man, however, did not rise again.

CHAPTER III

LOST in reverie, the stranger stood motionless on the Embankment. The racket of the city was behind him. At his feet lay a drowned world, its lights choking in the Thames. It was London, as it will be on the last day.

With an effort he roused himself and took Andrew's arm.

" The body will soon be recovered," he said, in a voice of great dejection, "and people will talk. Let us go."

They retraced their steps up Arundel Street.

" Now," said Andrew's companion, "tell me who you are."

Andrew would have preferred to hear who the stranger was. In the circumstances he felt that he had almost a right to know. But this was not a man to brook interference.

" If you will answer me one question," the young Scotchman said humbly, " I shall tell you everything."

His reveries had made Andrew quick-witted, and he had the judicial mind which prevents one's judging another rashly. Besides, his hankering after this man had already suggested an exculpation for him.

" You are a Radical ? " he asked eagerly.

The stranger's brows contracted. " Young man," he said, " though all the Radicals, and Liberals, and Conservatives who ever addressed the House of Commons were in ——, I would not stoop to pick them up, though I could gather them by the gross."

He said this without an Irish accent, and Andrew felt that he had better begin his story at once.

He told everything.

As his tale neared its conclusion his companion scanned him narrowly.

If the stranger's magnanimous countenance did not beam down in sympathy upon the speaker, it was because surprise and gratification filled it.

Only once an ugly look came into his eyes. That was when Andrew had reached the middle of his second testimonial.

The young man saw the look, and at the same time felt the hold on his arm become a grip.

His heart came into his mouth. He gulped it down, and, with what was perhaps a judicious sacrifice, jumped the remainder of his testimonials.

When the stranger heard how he had been tracked through the streets, he put his head to the side to think.

It was a remarkable compliment to his abstraction that Andrew paused involuntarily in his story and waited.

He felt that his future was in the balance. Those sons of peers may faintly realise his position whose parents have hesitated whether to make statesmen or cattle-dealers of them.

" I don't mind telling you," the stranger said at last, " that your case has been under consideration. When we left the Embankment my intention was to dispose of you in a doorway. But your story moves me strangely. Could I be certain that you felt the sacredness of human life — as I fear no boy can feel it — I should be tempted to ask you instead to become one of us."

There was something in this remark about the sacredness of human life that was not what Andrew expected, and his answer died unspoken.

" Youth," continued the stranger, "is enthusiasm, but not enthusiasm in a straight line. We are impotent in directing it, like a boy with a toy engine. How carefully the child sets it off, how soon it goes off the rails! So youth is wrecked. The slightest obstacle sends it off at a tangent. The vital force expended in a wrong direction does evil instead of good. You know the story of Atalanta. It has always been misread. She was the type not of woman but of youth, and Hippomenes personated age. He was the slower runner, but he won the race; and yet how beautiful, even where it runs to riot, must enthusiasm be in such a cause as ours!"

"If Atalanta had been Scotch," said Andrew, "she would not have lost that race for a pound of apples."

The stranger regarded him longingly, like a father only prevented by state reasons from embracing his son.

He murmured something that Andrew hardly caught.

It sounded like:

"Atalanta would have been better dead."

"Your nationality is in your favour," he said, "and you have served your apprenticeship to our calling. You have been tending towards us ever since you came to London. You are an apple ripe for plucking, and if you are not plucked now you will fall. I would fain take you by the hand, and yet —"

"And yet?"

"And yet I hesitate. You seem a youth of the fairest promise; but how often have I let these impulses deceive me! You talk of logic, but is it more than talk? Man, they say, is a reasonable being. They are wrong. He is only a being capable of reason."

"Try me," said Andrew.

The stranger resumed in a lower key:

"You do not understand what you ask as yet,"

he said; " still less what we would ask in return of you."

" I have seen something to-day," said Andrew.

" But you are mistaken in its application. You think I followed the man lately deceased as pertinaciously as you followed me. You are wrong. When you met me in Chancery Lane I was in pursuit of a gentleman to whose case I have devoted myself for several days. It has interested me much. There is no reason why I should conceal his name. It is one honoured in this country, Sir Wilfrid Lawson. He looked in on his man of business, which delayed me at the shop-window of which you have spoken. I waited for him, and I thought I had him this time. But you see I lost him in the Strand, after all."

" But the other, then," Andrew asked, " who was he ? "

" Oh, I picked him up at Charing Cross. He was better dead."

" I think," said Andrew, hopefully, " that my estimate of the sacredness of human life is sufficiently high for your purpose. If that is the only point —"

" Ah, they all say that until they join. I remember an excellent young man who came among us for a time. He seemed discreet beyond his years, and we expected great things of him. But it was the old story. For young men the cause is as demoralizing as boarding schools are for girls."

" What did he do ? "

" It went to his head. He took a bedroom in Pall Mall and sat at the window with an electric rifle picking them off on the door-steps of the clubs. It was a noble idea, but of course it imperilled the very existence of the society. He was a curate."

" What became of him ? " asked Andrew.

" He is better dead," said the stranger, softly.

" And the Society you speak of, what is it ? "

" The S. D. W. S. P."

" The S. D. W. S. P. ? "

" Yes, the Society for Doing Without Some People."

They were in Holborn, but turned up Southampton Row for quiet.

" You have told me," said the stranger, now speaking rapidly, " that at times you have felt tempted to take your life, that life for which you will one day have to account. Suicide is the coward's refuge. You are miserable ? When a young man knows that, he is happy. Misery is but preparing for an old age of delightful reminiscence. You say that London has no work for you, that the functions to which you looked forward are everywhere discharged by another. That need not drive you to despair. If it proves that someone should die, does it necessarily follow that the someone is you ? "

" But is not the other's life as sacred as mine ? "

" That is his concern."

" Then you would have me —"

" Certainly not. You are a boxer without employment, whom I am showing what to hit. In such a case as yours the Society would be represented by a third party, whose decision would be final. As an interested person you would have to stand aside."

" I don't understand."

" The arbitrator would settle if you should go."

Andrew looked blank.

" Go ? " he repeated.

" It is a euphemism for die," said his companion a little impatiently. " This is a trivial matter, and hardly worth going into at any length. It shows our process, however, and the process reveals the true character of the organization. As I have already mentioned, the Society takes for its first principle the sanctity of human life. Everyone who has mixed much among his fellow-creatures must be aware that this is adulterated, so to speak, by numbers of spurious existences. Many of these are a nuisance to themselves. Others may at an earlier period have been lives of great promise and fulfilment. In the case of the latter, how sad to think that they should be dragged out into worthlessness or dishonour, all for want of a friendly hand to snap them short ! In the lower form of life the process of preying upon animals whose work is accomplished — that is, of weeding — goes on continually. Man must, of course, be more cautious. The grand function of the Society is to find out the persons who have a claim on it, and in the interests of humanity to lay their condition before them. After that it is in the majority of cases for themselves to decide whether they will go or stay on."

"But," said Andrew, "had the gentleman in the Thames consented to go?"

"No, that was a case where assistance had to be given. He had been sounded, though."

"And do you find," asked Andrew, "that many of them are — agreeable?"

"I admit," said the stranger, "that so far that has been our chief difficulty. Even the men we looked upon as certainties have fallen short of our expectations. There is Mallock, now, who said that life was not worth living. I called on him only last week, fully expecting him to meet me half-way."

"And he didn't?"

"Mallock was a great disappointment," said the stranger, with genuine pain in his voice.

He liked Mallock.

"However," he added, brightening, "his case comes up for hearing at the next meeting. If I have two-thirds of the vote we proceed with it."

"But how do the authorities take it?" asked Andrew.

" Pooh ! " said the stranger.

Andrew, however, could not think so.

" It is against the law, you know," he said.

" The law winks at it," the stranger said. " Law has its feelings as well as we. We have two London magistrates and a minister on the executive, and the Lord Chief Justice is an honorary member."

Andrew raised his eyes.

" This, of course, is private," continued the stranger. " These men join on the understanding that if anything comes out they deny all connection with us. But they have the thing at heart. I have here a very kind letter from Gladstone — "

He felt in his pockets.

" I seem to have left it at home. However, its purport was that he hoped we would not admit Lord Salisbury an honorary member."

" Why not ? "

" Well, the Society has power to take from its numbers, so far as ordinary members are concerned, but it is considered discourteous to reduce the honorary list."

" Then why have honorary members ? " asked Andrew in a burst of enthusiasm.

" It is a necessary precaution. They subscribe largely too. Indeed, the association is now established on a sound commercial basis. We are paying six per cent."

" None of these American preachers who come

over to this country are honorary members?" asked Andrew, anxiously.

"No; one of them made overtures to us, but we would not listen to him. Why?"

"Oh, nothing," said Andrew.

"To do the honorary list justice," said his companion, "it gave us one fine fellow in our honorary president. He is dead now."

Andrew looked up.

"No, we had nothing to do with it. It was Thomas Carlyle."

Andrew raised his hat.

"Though he was over eighty years of age," continued the stranger. "Carlyle would hardly rest content with merely giving us his countenance. He wanted to be a working member. It was he who mentioned Froude's name to us."

"For honorary membership?"

"Not at all. Froude would hardly have completed the 'Reminiscences' had it not been that we could never make up our minds between him and Freeman."

Youth is subject to sudden fits of despondency. Its hopes go up and down like a bucket in a drawwell.

"They'll never let me join," cried Andrew, sorrowfully.

His companion pressed his hand.

"Three black balls exclude," he said, "but you

have the president on your side. With my intro-
duction you will be admitted a probationer, and
after that everything depends on yourself."

" I thought you must be the president from the
first," said Andrew, reverently.

He had not felt so humble since the first day he
went to the University and walked past and repast
it, frightened to go in.

" How long," he asked, " does the period of
probation last ? "

" Three months. Then you send in a thesis,
and if it is considered satisfactory you become a
member."

" And if it isn't ? "

The president did not say.

" A thesis," he said, " is generally a paper with
a statement of the line of action you propose to
adopt, subject to the Society's approval. Each
member has his specialty — as law, art, divinity,
literature, and the like."

" Does the probationer devote himself exclusively during these three months to his thesis ? "

" On the contrary, he never has so much liberty
as at this period. He is expected to be practising."

" Practising ? "

" Well, experimenting, getting his hand in, so
to speak. The member acts under instructions only,
but the probationer just does what he thinks best."

" There is a man on my stair," said Andrew,

after a moment's consideration, "who asks his friends in every Friday night, and recites to them with his door open. I think I should like to begin with him."

"As a society we do not recognise these private cases. The public gain is so infinitesimal. We had one probationer who constructed a very ingenious water-butt for boys. Another had a scheme for clearing the streets of the people who get in the way. He got into trouble about some perambulators. Let me see your hands."

They stopped at a lamp-post.

"They are large, which is an advantage," said the president, fingering Andrew's palms; "but are they supple?"

Andrew had thought very little about it, and he did not quite comprehend.

"The hands," explained the president, "are perhaps the best natural weapon; but, of course, there are different ways of doing it."

The young Scotchman's brain, however, could not keep pace with his companion's words, and the president looked about him for an illustration.

They stopped at Gower Street station and glanced at the people coming out.

None of them was of much importance, but the president left them alone.

Andrew saw what he meant now, and could not but admire his forbearance.

They turned away, but just as they emerged into the blaze of Tottenham Court Road they ran into two men, warmly shaking hands with each other before they parted. One of them wore an eye-glass.

" Chamberlain ! " exclaimed the president, rushing after him.

" Did you recognise the other ? " said Andrew, panting at his heels.

" No ! who was it ? "

" Stead, of the ' Pall Mall Gazette.' "

" Great God," cried the president, " two at a time ! "

He turned and ran back. Then he stopped irresolutely. He could not follow the one for thought of the other.

CHAPTER IV

THE London cabman's occupation consists in dodging thoroughfares under repair.

Numbers of dingy streets have been flung about to help him. There is one of these in Bloomsbury, which was originally discovered by a student while looking for the British Museum. It runs a hundred yards in a straight line, then stops, like a stranger who has lost his way, and hurries by another route out of the neighbourhood.

The houses are dull, except one, just where it doubles, which is gloomy.

This house is divided into sets of chambers and has a new frontage, but it no longer lets well. A few years ago there were two funerals from it within a fortnight, and soon afterward another of the tenants was found at the foot of the stair with his neck broken. These fatalities gave the house a bad name, as such things do in London.

It was here that Andrew's patron, the president, lived.

To the outcast from work to get an object in life is to be born again. Andrew bustled to the

224

president's chambers on the Saturday night following the events already described, with his chest well set.

His springy step echoed of wages in the hearts of the unemployed. Envious eyes, following his swaggering staff, could not see that but a few days before he had been as the thirteenth person at a dinner-party.

Such a change does society bring about when it empties a chair for the superfluous man.

It may be wondered that he felt so sure of himself, for the night had still to decide his claims.

Andrew, however, had thought it all out in his solitary lodgings, and had put fear from him. He felt his failings and allowed for every one of them, but he knew his merits too, and his testimonials were in his pocket. Strength of purpose was his weak point, and, though the good of humanity was his loadstar, it did not make him quite forget self.

It may not be possible to serve both God and mammon, but since Adam the world has been at it. We ought to know by this time.

The Society for Doing Without was as immoral as it certainly was illegal. The president's motives were not more disinterested than his actions were defensible. He even deserved punishment.

All these things may be. The great social question is not to be solved in a day. It never will be solved if those who take it by the beard are not given an unbiassed hearing.

Those were the young Scotchman's views when the president opened the door to him, and what he saw and heard that night strengthened them.

It was characteristic of Andrew's host that at such a time he could put himself in the young man's place.

He took his hand and looked him in the face more like a physician than a mere acquaintance. Then he drew him aside into an empty room.

"Let me be the first to congratulate you," he said; "you are admitted."

Andrew took a long breath, and the president considerately turned away his head until the young probationer had regained his composure. Then he proceeded:

"The society only asks from its probationers the faith which it has in them. They take no oath. We speak in deeds. The Brotherhood do not recognise the possibility of treachery; but they· are prepared to cope with it if it comes. Better far, Andrew Riach, to be in your grave, dead and rotten and forgotten, than a traitor to the cause."

The president's voice trembled with solemnity.

He stretched forth his hands, slowly repeating the words, "dead and rotten and forgotten," until his wandering eyes came to rest on the young man's neck.

226

Andrew drew back a step and bowed silently, as he had seen many a father do at a christening in the kirk at Wheens.

"You will shortly," continued the president, with a return to his ordinary manner, "hear an address on female suffrage from one of the noblest women in the land. It will be your part to listen. To-night you will both hear and see strange things. Say nothing. Evince no surprise. Some members are irritable. Come!"

Once more he took Andrew by the hand, and led him into the meeting-room; and still his eyes were fixed on the probationer's neck. There seemed to be something about it that he liked.

It was not then, with the committee all around him, but long afterwards at Wheens, that Andrew was struck by the bareness of the chambers.

Without the president's presence they had no character.

The trifles were absent that are to a room what expression is to the face.

The tenant might have been a medical student who knew that it was not worth while to unpack his boxes.

The only ornament on the walls was an elaborate sketch by a member, showing the arrangement of the cellars beneath the premises of the Young Men's Christian Association.

There were a dozen men in the room, including

the president of the Birmingham branch association and two members who had just returned from a visit to Edinburgh. These latter had already submitted their report.

The president introduced Andrew to the committee, but not the committee to him. Several of them he recognized from the portraits in the shop windows.

They stood or sat in groups looking over a probationer's thesis. It consisted of diagrams of machinery.

Andrew did not see the sketches, though they were handed round separately for inspection, but he listened eagerly to the president's explanations.

" The first," said the president, " is a beautiful little instrument worked by steam. Having placed his head on the velvet cushion D, the subject can confidently await results.

" No. 2 is the same model on a larger scale.

" As yet 3 can be of little use to us. It includes a room 13 feet by 11. X is the windows and other apertures; and these being closed up and the subjects admitted, all that remains to be done is to lock the door from the outside and turn on the gas. E, F, and K are couches, and L is a square inch of glass through which results may be noted.

" The speciality of 4, which is called the ' water cure,' is that it is only workable on water. It is generally admitted that release by drowning is the pleasantest of all deaths; and, indeed, 4, speaking roughly, is a boat with a hole in the bottom. It is so simple that a child could work it. C is the plug.

"No. 5 is an intricate instrument. The advantage claimed for it is that it enables a large number of persons to leave together."

While the thesis was under discussion, the attendance was increased by a few members specially interested in the question of female suffrage. Andrew observed that several of these wrote something on a piece of paper which lay on the table with a pencil beside it, before taking their seats.

He stretched himself in the direction of this paper, but subsided as he caught the eyes of two of the company riveted on his neck.

From that time until he left the rooms one member or other was staring at his neck. Andrew looked anxiously in the glass over the mantelpiece but could see nothing wrong.

The paper on the table merely contained such jottings as these : —

"Robert Buchanan has written another play."

"Schnadhörst is in town."

"Ashmead Bartlett walks in Temple Gardens 3 to 4."

"Clement Scott (?)"

"Query: Is there a dark passage near Hyndman's (Socialist's) house?"

" Talmage.   Address, Midland Hotel."

" Andrew Lang (?) "

Andrew was a good deal interested in woman's suffrage, and the debate on this question in the students' society at Edinburgh, when he spoke for an hour and five minutes, is still remembered by the janitor who had to keep the door until the meeting closed.

Debating societies, like the company of reporters, engender a familiarity of reference to eminent persons, and Andrew had in his time struck down the champions of woman's rights as a boy plays with his ninepins.

To be brought face to face with a lady whose name is a household word wheresoever a few Scotchmen can meet and resolve themselves into an argument was another matter.

It was with no ordinary mingling of respect with curiosity that he stood up with the others to greet Mrs. Fawcett as the president led her into the room.   The young man's face, as he looked upon her for the first time, was the best book this remarkable woman ever wrote.

The proceedings were necessarily quiet, and the president had introduced their guest to the meeting without Andrew's hearing a word.

He was far away in a snow-swept University quadrangle on a windy night, when Mrs. Fawcett rose to her feet.

Some one flung open the window, for the place was close, and immediately the skirl of a bagpiper broke the silence.

It might have been the devil that rushed into the room.

Still Andrew dreamed on.

The guest paused.

The members looked at each other, and the president nodded to one of them.

He left the room, and about two minutes afterwards the music suddenly ceased.

Andrew woke with a start in time to see him return, write two words in the members' book, and resume his seat. Mrs. Fawcett then began.

" I have before me," she said, turning over the leaves of a bulky manuscript, " a great deal of matter bearing on the question of woman's rights, which at such a meeting as this may be considered read. It is mainly historical, and while I am prepared to meet with hostile criticism from the society, I assume that the progress our agitation has made, with its disappointments, its trials, and its triumphs, has been followed more or less carefully by you all.

" Nor shall I, after the manner of speakers on such an occasion, pay you the doubtful compliment of fulsomely extolling your aims before your face.

" I come at once to the question of woman's

231

rights in so far as the society can affect them, and I ask of you a consideration of my case with as little prejudice as men can be expected to approach it.

" In the constitution of the society, as it has been explained to me, I notice chiefly two things which would have filled me with indignation twenty years ago, but only remind me how far we are from the goal of our ambition now.

" The first is a sin of omission, the second one of commission, and the latter is the more to be deprecated in that you made it with your eyes open, after full discussion, while the other came about as a matter of course.

" I believe I am right in saying that the membership of this society is exclusively male, and also that no absolute veto has been placed on female candidature.

" As a matter of fact, it never struck the founders that such a veto in black and white was necessary. When they drew up the rules of membership the other sex never fell like a black shadow on the paper; it was forgotten. We owe our eligibility to many other offices (generally disputed at law) to the same accident. In short, the unwritten law of the *argumentum ad crinolinam* puts us to the side."

Having paid the society the compliment of believing that, however much it differed from her views, it would not dismiss them with a laugh,

Mrs. Fawcett turned to the question of woman's alleged physical limitations.

She said much on this point that Andrew saw could not be easily refuted, but, interesting though she made it, we need not follow her over beaten ground.

So far the members had given her the courteous non-attention which thoughtful introductory remarks can always claim. It was when she reached her second head that they fastened upon her words.

Then Andrew had seen no sharper audience since he was one of a Scotch congregation on the scent of a heretic.

"At a full meeting of committee," said Mrs. Fawcett, with a ring of bitterness in her voice, "you passed a law that women should not enjoy the advantages of the association. Be they ever so eminent, their sex deprives them of your care. You take up the case of a petty maker of books because his tea-leaf solutions weary you, and you put a stop to him with an enthusiasm worthy of a nobler object.

"But the woman is left to decay.

"This society at its noblest was instituted for taking strong means to prevent men's slipping down the ladder it has been such a toil to them to mount, but the women who have climbed as high as they can fall from rung to rung.

"There are female nuisances as well as male; I

233

presume no one here will gainsay me that. But you do not know them officially. The politicians who joke about three acres and a cow, the writers who are comic about mothers-in-law, the very boot-blacks have your solicitude, but you ignore their complements in the softer sex.

"Yet you call yourselves a society for suppressing excrescences! Your president tells me you are at present inquiring for the address of the man who signs himself 'Paterfamilias' in the 'Times'; but the letters from 'A British Matron' are of no account.

"I do not need to be told how Dr. Smith, the fashionable physician, was precipitated down that area the other day; but what I do ask is, why should he be taken and all the lady doctors left?

"Their degrees are as good as his. You are too 'manly,' you say, to arrest their course. Is injustice manliness? We have another name for it. We say you want the pluck.

"I suppose every one of you has been reading a very able address recently delivered at the meeting of the Social Science Congress. I refer to my friend Mrs. Kendal's paper on the moral aspect of the drama in this country.

"It is a powerful indictment of the rank and file of her professional brothers and sisters, and nowhere sadder, more impressive, or more unanswerable than where she speaks of the involuntary fall of the actor into social snobbishness and professional clap-trap.

" I do not know how the paper affected you. But since reading it I have asked in despair, how can this gifted lady continue to pick her way between the snares with which the stage is beset?

" Is it possible that the time may come when she will advertise by photographs and beg from reporters the 'pars' she now so scathingly criticises? Nay, when I look upon the drop scene at the St. James's Theatre, I ask myself if the deterioration has not already set in.

"Gentlemen, is this a matter of indifference to you? But why do I ask? Has not Mrs. Lynn Linton another article in the new 'Nineteenth Century' that makes her worthy your attention? They are women, and the sex is outside your sphere."

It was nearly twelve o'clock when Mrs. Fawcett finished her address, and the society had adopted the good old rule of getting to bed betimes. Thus it was afterwards that Andrew learned how long and carefully the society had already considered the advisability of giving women equal rights with men.

As he was leaving the chambers the president slipped something into his hand. He held it there until he reached his room.

On the way a man struck against him, scanned

him piercingly, and then shuffled off. He was muffled up, but Andrew wondered if he had not seen him at the meeting.

The young Scotchman had an uneasy feeling that his footsteps were dodged.

As soon as he reached home he unfolded the scrap of paper that had been pushed into his hand. It merely contained these words —

"Cover up your neck."

CHAPTER V

On the following Tuesday Andrew met the president by appointment at the Marble Arch.

Until he had received his final instructions he was pledged not to begin, and he had passed these two intervening days staring at his empty fireplace.

They shook hands silently and passed into the Park. The president was always thoughtful in a crowd.

"In such a gathering as this," said Andrew, pointing an imaginary pistol at a lecturer on Socialism, "you could hardly go wrong to let fly."

"You must not speak like that," the president said gently, "or we shall soon lose you. Your remark, however, opens the way for what I have to say. You have never expressed any curiosity as to your possible fate. I hope this is not because you under-estimate the risks. If the authorities saw you 'letting fly' as you term it, promiscuously, or even at a given object, they would treat you as no better than a malefactor."

237

"I thought that all out yesterday," said Andrew, "and I am amazed at the society's success in escaping detection."

"I feared this," said the president. "You are mistaken. We don't always escape detection. Sometimes we are caught —"

"Caught?"

"Yes, and hanged."

"But if that is so, why does it not get into the papers?"

"The papers are full of it."

Andrew looked incredulous.

"In the present state of the law," said the president, "motive in a murder goes for nothing However iniquitous this may be — and I do not. attempt to defend it — we accept it as a fact. Your motives may have been unexceptionable, but they hang you all the same. Thus our members when apprehended preserve silence on this point, or say that they are Fenians. This is to save the society. The man who got fifteen years the other day for being found near St. Stephen's with six infernal machines in his pockets was really one of us. He was taking them to be repaired."

"And the other who got ten years the week before?"

"He was from America, but it was for one of our affairs that he was sentenced. He was quite innocent. You see the dynamiters, vulgarly so

238

called, are playing into our hands. Suspicion naturally falls on them. He was our fifth."

"I had no idea of this," murmured Andrew.

"You see what a bad name does," said the president. "Let this be a warning to you, Andrew."

"But is this quite fair?"

"As for that, they like it — the leading spirits, I mean. It gives them a reputation. Besides, they hurt as well as help us. It was after their appearance that the authorities were taught to be distrustful. You have little idea of the precautions taken nowadays. There is Sir William Harcourt, for instance, who is attended by policemen everywhere. I used to go home from the House behind him nightly, but I could never get him alone. I have walked in the very shadow of that man, but always in a company."

"You were never arrested yourself?" asked Andrew.

"I was once, but we substituted a probationer."

"Then did he — was he — "

"Yes, poor fellow."

"Is that often done?"

"Sometimes. You perhaps remember the man who went over the Embankment the night we met? Well, if I had been charged with that, you would have had to be hanged."

Andrew took a seat to collect his thoughts.

"Was that why you seemed to take to me so much?" he asked, wistfully.

"It was only one reason," said the president, soothingly. "I liked you from the first."

"But I don't see," said Andrew, "why I should have suffered for your action."

For the moment, his veneration for this remarkable man hung in the balance.

"It would have been for the society's sake," said the president, simply; "probationers are hardly missed."

His face wore a pained look, but there was no reproach in his voice.

Andrew was touched.

He looked the apology, which, as a Scotchman, he could not go the length of uttering.

"Before I leave you to-day," said the president, turning to a pleasanter subject, "I shall give you some money. We do not, you understand, pay our probationers a fixed salary."

"It is more, is it not," said Andrew, "in the nature of a scholarship?"

"Yes, a scholarship — for the endowment of research. You see we do not tie you down to any particular line of study. Still, I shall be happy to hear of any programme you may have drawn up."

Andrew hesitated. He did not know that, to the president, he was an open book.

"I dare say I can read your thoughts," said his

companion. " There is an eminent person whom you would like to make your first ? "

Andrew admitted that this was so.

" I do not ask any confidences of you," continued the president, " nor shall I discourage ambition. But I hope, Andrew, you have only in view the greatest good of the greatest number. At such a time, it is well for the probationer to ask himself two questions: Is it not self-glorification that prompts me to pick this man out from among so many? and, Am I actuated by any personal animosity? If you cannot answer both these questions in the negative, it is time to ask a third, Should I go on with this undertaking? "

" In this case," said Andrew, " I do not think it is self-glory, and I am sure it is not spite. He is a man I have a very high opinion of."

" A politician? Remember that we are above party considerations."

" He is a politician," said Andrew, reluctantly, " but it is his politics I admire."

" And you are sure his time has come? Then how do you propose to set about it? "

" I thought of calling at his house, and putting it to him."

The president's countenance fell.

" Well, well," he said, " that may answer. But there is no harm in bearing in mind that persuasion is not necessarily a passive force. Without going the length of removing him yourself, you know, you could put temptation in his way."

" If I know my man," said Andrew, " that will not be required."

The president had drunk life's disappointments to the dregs, but it was not in his heart to damp the youth's enthusiasm.

Experience he knew to be a commodity for which we pay a fancy price.

" After that," said Andrew, " I thought of Henry Irving."

" We don't kill actors," his companion said.

It was Andrew's countenance's turn to fall now.

" We don't have time for it," the president explained. " When the society was instituted, we took a few of them, but merely to get our hands in. We didn't want to bungle good cases, you see, and it did not matter so much for them."

" How did you do it ? "

" We waited at the stage-door, and went off with the first person who came out, male or female."

" But I understood you did not take up women ? "

" Nor do we. Theatrical people constitute a sex by themselves — like curates."

" Then can't I even do the man who stands at the theatre doors, all shirt-front and diamonds ? "

The president shivered.

" If you happen to be passing, at any rate," he said.

" And surely some of the playwrights would be better dead. They must see that themselves."

" They have had their chance," said the president. Despite his nationality, Andrew had not heard the story, so the president told it him.

" Many years ago, when the drama was in its infancy, some young men from Stratford-on-Avon and elsewhere resolved to build a theatre in London.

" The times, however, were moral, and no one would imperil his soul so far as to give them a site.

" One night, they met in despair, when suddenly the room was illumined by lightning, and they saw the devil in the midst of them.

" He has always been a large proprietor in London, and he had come to strike a bargain with them. They could have as many sites as they chose, on one condition. Every year they must send him a dramatist.

" You see he was willing to take his chance of the players.

" The compact was made, and up to the present time it has been religiously kept. But this year, as the day drew near, found the managers very uneasy. They did what they could. They forwarded the best man they had."

" What happened ? " asked Andrew, breathlessly.

" The devil sent him back," said the president.

CHAPTER VI

It was one Sunday forenoon, on such a sunny day as slovenly men seize upon to wash their feet and have it over, that Andrew set out to call on Mr. Labouchere.

The leaves in the squares were green, and the twittering of the birds among the boughs was almost gay enough to charm him out of the severity of countenance which a Scotchman wears on a Sunday with his blacks.

Andrew could not help regarding the mother-of-pearl sky as a favourable omen. Several times he caught himself becoming light-hearted.

He got the great Radical on the door-step, just setting out for church.

The two men had not met before, but Andrew was a disciple in the school in which the other taught.

Between man and man formal introductions are humbug.

Andrew explained in a few words the nature of his visit, and received a cordial welcome.

"But I could call again," he said, observing the hymn-book in the other's hand.

"Nonsense," said Mr. Labouchere heartily; "it must be business before pleasure. Mind the step."

So saying, he led his visitor into a cheerful snuggery at the back of the house. It was furnished with a careful contempt for taste, and the first thing that caught Andrew's eye was a pot of apple jam on a side table.

"I have no gum," Mr. Labouchere explained hastily.

A handsomely framed picture, representing Truth lying drowned at the bottom of a well, stood on the mantel-piece; indeed, there were many things in the room that, on another occasion, Andrew would have been interested to hear the history of.

He could not but know, however, that at present he was to some extent an intruder, and until he had fully explained his somewhat delicate business he would not feel at ease.

Though argumentative, Andrew was essentially a shy, proud man.

It was very like Mr. Labouchere to leave him to tell his story in his own way, only now and then, at the outset, interjecting a humorous remark, which we here omit,

"I hope," said Andrew earnestly, "that you will not think it fulsome on my part to say how much I like you. In your public utterances you have let it be known what value you set on pretty

245

phrases; but I speak the blunt truth, as you have taught it. I am only a young man, perhaps awkward and unpolished —"

Here Andrew paused, but as Mr. Labouchere did not say anything he resumed.

"That as it may be, I should like you to know that your political speeches have become part of my life. When I was a student it seemed to me that the Radicalism of so called advanced thinkers was a half-hearted sham; I had no interest in politics at all until I read your attack — one of them — on the House of Lords. That day marked an epoch in my life. I used to read the University library copy of 'Truth' from cover to cover. Sometimes I carried it into the class-room. That was not allowed. I took it up my waistcoat. In those days I said that if I wrote a book I would dedicate it to you without permission, and London, when I came to it, was to me the town where you lived."

There was a great deal of truth in this; indeed, Mr. Labouchere's single-hearted enthusiasm — be his politics right or wrong — is well calculated to fascinate young men.

If it was slightly over-charged, the temptation was great. Andrew was keenly desirous of carrying his point, and he wanted his host to see that he was only thinking of his good.

"Well, but what is it you would have me do?"

asked Mr. Labouchere, who often had claimants
on his bounty and his autographs.

" I want you," said Andrew eagerly, "to die."

The two men looked hard at each other. There
was not even a clock in the room to break the
silence. At last the statesman spoke.

" Why ? " he asked.

His visitor sank back in his chair relieved.

He had put all his hopes in the other's common-
sense.

It had never failed Mr. Labouchere, and now it
promised not to fail Andrew.

" I am anxious to explain that," the young man
said glibly. " If you can look at yourself with the
same eyes with which you see other people, it won't
take long. Make a looking-glass of me, and it is
done.

" You have now reached a high position in the
worlds of politics and literature, to which you have
cut your way unaided.

" You are a great satirist, combining instruction
with amusement, a sort of comic Carlyle.

" You hate shams so much that if man had been
constructed for it I dare say you would kick at
yourself.

" You have your enemies, but the very persons
who blunt their weapons on you do you the honour
of sharpening them on ' Truth.' In short, you
have reached the summit of your fame, and you

are too keen a man of the world not to know that fame is a touch-and-go thing."

Andrew paused.

"Go on," said Mr. Labouchere.

"Well, you have now got fame, honour, everything for which it is legitimate in man to strive.

"So far back as I can remember, you have had the world laughing with you. But you know what human nature is.

"There comes a morning to all wits, when their public wakes to find them bores. The fault may not be the wit's, but what of that? The result is the same.

"Wits are like theatres: they may have a glorious youth and prime, but their old age is dismal. To the outsider, like myself, signs are not wanting — to continue the figure of speech — that you have put on your last successful piece.

"Can you say candidly that your last Christmas number was more than a reflection of its predecessors, or that your remarks this year on the Derby day took as they did the year before?

"Surely the most incisive of our satirists will not let himself degenerate into an illustration of Mr. Herbert Spencer's theory that man repeats himself, like history.

"Mr. Labouchere, sir, to those of us who have grown up in your inspiration it would indeed be pitiful if this were so."

248

Andrew's host turned nervously in his chair.

Probably he wished that he had gone to church now.

"You need not be alarmed," he said, with a forced smile.

"You will die," cried Andrew, "before they send you to the House of Lords?"

"In which case the gain would be all to those left behind."

"No," said Andrew, who now felt that he had as good as gained the day; "there could not be a greater mistake.

"Suppose it happened to-night, or even put it off to the end of the week; see what would follow.

"The ground you have lost so far is infinitesimal. It would be forgotten in the general regret.

"Think of the newspaper placards next morning, some of them perhaps edged with black; the leaders in every London paper and in all the prominent provincial ones; the six columns obituary in the 'Times'; the paragraphs in the 'World'; the motion by Mr. Gladstone or Mr. Healy for the adjournment of the House; the magazine articles; the promised memoirs; the publication of posthumous papers; the resolution in the Northampton Town Council; the statue in Hyde Park! With such a recompense where would be the sacrifice?"

Mr. Labouchere rose and paced the room in great mental agitation.

"Now look at the other side of the picture," said Andrew, rising and following him: "'Truth' reduced to threepence, and then to a penny; yourself confused with Tracy Turnerelli or Martin Tupper; your friends running when you looked like jesting; the House emptying, the reporters shutting their note-books as you rose to speak; the great name of Labouchere become a synonym for bore!"

They presented a strange picture in that room, its owner's face now a greyish white, his supplicant shaking with a passion that came out in perspiration.

With trembling hand Mr. Labouchere flung open the window. The room was stifling.

There was a smell of new-mown hay in the air, a gentle breeze tipped the well-trimmed hedge with life, and the walks crackled in the heat.

But a stone's throw distant the sun was bathing in the dimpled Thames.

There was a cawing of rooks among the tall trees, and a church-bell tinkled in the ivy far away across the river.

Mr. Labouchere was far away too.

He was a round-cheeked boy again, smothering his kitten in his pinafore, prattling of Red Riding Hood by his school-mistress's knee, and guddling in the brook for minnows.

And now — and now!

It was a beautiful world, and, ah, life is sweet!
He pressed his fingers to his forehead.

"Leave me," he said hoarsely.

Andrew put his hand upon the shoulder of the
man he loved so well.

"Be brave," he said; "do it in whatever way
you prefer. A moment's suffering, and all will be
over."

He spoke gently. There is always something
infinitely pathetic in the sight of a strong man in
pain.

Mr. Labouchere turned upon him.

"Go," he cried, "or I will call the servants."

"You forget," said Andrew, "that I am your
guest."

But his host only pointed to the door.

Andrew felt a great sinking at his heart. They
prate who say it is success that tries a man. He
flung himself at Mr. Labouchere's feet.

"Think of the public funeral," he cried.

His host seized the bell-rope and pulled it
violently.

"If you will do it," said Andrew solemnly, "I
promise to lay flowers on your grave every day till
I die."

"John," said Mr. Labouchere, "show this gentleman out."

Andrew rose.

"You refuse?" he asked.

"I do."

"You won't think it over? If I call again, say on Thursday —"

"John!" said Mr. Labouchere.

Andrew took up his hat. His host thought he had gone. But in the hall his reflection in a looking-glass reminded the visitor of something. He put his head in at the doorway again.

"Would you mind telling me," he said, "whether you see anything peculiar about my neck?"

"It seems a good neck to twist," Mr. Labouchere answered, a little savagely.

Andrew then withdrew.

CHAPTER VII

THIS unexpected rebuff from Mr. Labouchere rankled for many days in Andrew's mind. Had he been proposing for the great statesman's hand he could not have felt it more. Perhaps he did not make sufficient allowance for Mr. Labouchere; it is always so easy to advise.

But to rage at a man (or woman) is the proof that we can adore them; it is only his loved ones who infuriate a Scotchman.

There were moments when Andrew said to himself that he had nothing more to live for.

Then he would upbraid himself for having gone about it too hurriedly, and in bitter self-contempt strike his hand on the railings, as he rushed by.

Work is the sovereign remedy for this unhealthy state of mind, and fortunately Andrew had a great deal to do.

Gradually the wound healed, and he began to take an interest in Lord Randolph Churchill.

Every day the Flying Scotchman shoots its refuse of clever young men upon London who are too ambitious to do anything.

253

Andrew was not one of these.

Seeking to carry off one of the greatest prizes in his profession, he had aimed too high for a beginner.

When he realised this he apprenticed himself, so to speak, to the president, determined to acquire a practical knowledge of his art in all its branches. Though a very young man, he had still much to learn. It was only in his leisure moments that he gave way to dreams over a *magnum opus*.

But when he did set about it, which must be before his period of probation closed, he had made up his mind to be thorough.

The months thus passed quietly but not unprofitably in assisting the president, acquainting himself with the favourite resorts of interesting persons and composing his thesis.

At intervals the monotony was relieved by more strictly society work. On these occasions he played a part not dissimilar to that of a junior counsel.

The president found him invaluable in his raid on the gentlemen with umbrellas who read newspapers in the streets.

It was Andrew — though he never got the credit of it — who put his senior in possession of the necessary particulars about the comic writers whose subject is teetotalism and spinsters.

He was unwearying, indeed, in his efforts with regard to the comic journals generally, and the first man of any note that he disposed of was " Punch's " favourite artist on Scotch matters. This was in an alley off Fleet Street.

Andrew took a new interest in the House of Lords, and had a magnificent scheme for ending it in half an hour.

As the members could never be got together in any number, this fell through.

Lord Brabourne will remember the young man in a straw hat, with his neck covered up, who attended the House so regularly when it was announced that he was to speak. That was Andrew.

It was he who excitedly asked the Black Rod to point out Lord Sherbrooke, when it was intimated that this peer was preparing a volume of poems for the press.

In a month's time Andrew knew the likeliest places to meet these and other noble lords alone.

The publishing offices of " England," the only Conservative newspaper, had a fascination for him.

He got to know Mr. Ashmead Bartlett's hours of calling, until the sight of him on the pavement was accepted as a token that the proprietor was inside.

They generally reached the House of Commons about the same time.

Here Andrew's interest was discriminated among quite a number of members. Mr. Bradlaugh, Mr. Sexton, and Mr. Marjoribanks, the respected member for Berwickshire, were perhaps his favourites ;

but the one he dwelt with most pride on was Lord Randolph Churchill.

One night he gloated so long over Sir George Trevelyan leaning over Westminster Bridge that in the end he missed him.

When Andrew made up his mind to have a man he got to like him. This was his danger.

With press tickets, which he got very cheap, he often looked in at the theatres to acquaint himself with the faces and figures of the constant frequenters.

He drew capital pencil sketches of the leading critics in his note-book.

The gentleman next him that night at "Manteaux Noirs" would not have laughed so heartily if he had known why Andrew listened for his address to the cabman.

The young Scotchman resented people's merriment over nothing; sometimes he took the Underground Railway just to catch clerks at "Tit-Bits."

One afternoon he saw some way in front of him in Piccadilly a man with a young head on old shoulders.

Andrew recognized him by the swing of his stick; he could have identified his plaid among a hundred thousand morning coats. It was John Stuart Blackie, his favourite professor.

Since the young man graduated, his old preceptor had resigned his chair, and was now devoting his time to writing sonnets to himself in the Scotch newspapers.

Andrew could not bear to think of it, and quickened his pace to catch him up. But Blackie was in great form, humming "Scots wha hae." With head thrown back, staff revolving and chest inflated, he sang himself into a martial ecstasy, and, drumming cheerily on the doors with his fist, strutted along like a band of bagpipers with a clan behind him, until he had played himself out of Andrew's sight.

Far be it from our intention to maintain that Andrew was invariably successful. That is not given to any man.

Sometimes his hands slipped.

Had he learned the piano in his younger days this might not have happened. But if he had been a pianist the president would probably have wiped him out — and very rightly. There can be no doubt about male pianists.

Nor was the fault always Andrew's. When the society was founded, many far-seeing men had got wind of it, and had themselves elected honorary members before the committee realised what they were after.

This was a sore subject with the president; he shunned discussing it, and thus Andrew had frequently to discontinue cases after he was well on with them.

In this way much time was lost.

Andrew was privately thanked by the committee for one suggestion, which, for all he knows, may yet be carried out. The president had a wide interest in the press, and on one occasion he remarked to Andrew:

" Think of the snobs and the prigs who would be saved if the ' Saturday Review ' and the ' Spectator ' could be induced to cease publication ! "

Andrew thought it out, and then produced his scheme.

The battle of the clans on the North Inch of Perth had always seemed to him a master-stroke of diplomacy.

" Why," he said to the president, " not set the ' Saturday's ' staff against the ' Spectator's.' If about equally matched, they might exterminate each other."

So his days of probation passed, and the time drew nigh for Andrew to show what stuff was in him.

CHAPTER VIII

ANDREW had set apart July 31 for killing Lord Randolph Churchill.

As his term of probation was up in the second week of August, this would leave him nearly a fortnight to finish his thesis in.

On the 30th he bought a knife in Holborn suitable for his purpose. It had been his original intention to use an electric rifle, but those he was shown were too cumbrous for use in the streets.

The eminent statesman was residing at this time at the Grand Hotel, and Andrew thought to get him somewhere between Trafalgar Square and the House. Taking up his position in a window of Morley's Hotel at an early hour, he set himself to watch the windows opposite. The plan of the Grand was well known to him, for he had frequently made use of it as overlooking the National Liberal Club, whose membership he had already slightly reduced.

Turning his eyes to the private sitting-rooms, he soon discovered Lord Randolph busily writing in one of them.

Andrew had lunch at Morley's, so that he might

be prepared for any emergency. Lord Randolph wrote on doggedly through the forenoon, and Andrew hoped he would finish what he was at in case this might be his last chance.

It rained all through the afternoon. The thick drizzle seemed to double the width of the street, and even to Andrew's strained eyes the shadow in the room opposite was obscured.

His eyes wandered from the window to the hotel entrance, and as cab after cab rattled from it he became uneasy.

In ordinary circumstances he could have picked his man out anywhere, but in rain all men look alike. He could have dashed across the street and rushed from room to room of the Grand Hotel.

His self-restraint was rewarded.

Late in the afternoon Lord Randolph came to the window. The flashing waterproofs and scurrying umbrellas were a surprise to him, and he knitted his brows in annoyance.

By-and-by his face was convulsed with laughter.

He drew a chair to the window and stood on it. that he might have a better view of the pavement beneath.

For some twenty minutes he remained there smacking his thighs, his shoulders heaving with glee.

Andrew could not see what it was, but he formulated a theory.

Heavy blobs of rain that had gathered on the window-sill slowly released their hold from time to time and fell with a plump on the hats of passers-by. Lord Randolph was watching them.

Just as they were letting go he shook the window to make the wayfarers look up. They got the rain-drops full in the face, and then he screamed.

About six o'clock Andrew paid his bill hurriedly and ran downstairs. Lord Randolph had come to the window in his greatcoat. His follower waited for him outside. It was possible that he would take a hansom and drive straight to the House, but Andrew had reasons for thinking this unlikely. The rain had somewhat abated. Lord Randolph came out, put up his umbrella, and, glancing at the sky for a moment, set off briskly up St. Martin's Lane.

Andrew knew that he would not linger here, for they had done St. Martin's Lane already.

Lord Randolph's movements these last days had excited the Scotchman's curiosity. He had been doing the London streets systematically during his unoccupied afternoons. But it was difficult to discover what he was after.

It was the tobacconists' shops that attracted him.

He did not enter, only stood at the windows counting something.

He jotted down the result on a piece of paper and then sped on to the next shop.

In this way, with Andrew at his heels, he had done the whole of the W. C. district, St. James's, Oxford Street, Piccadilly, Bond Street, and the Burlington Arcade.

On this occasion he took the small thorough-fares lying between upper Regent Street and Tottenham Court Road. Beginning in Great Titchfield Street he went from tobacconist's to tobacconist's, sometimes smiling to himself, at other times frowning. Andrew scrutinised the windows as he left them, but could make nothing of it.

Not for the first time he felt that there could be no murder to-night unless he saw the paper first.

Lord Randolph devoted an hour to this work. Then he hailed a cab.

Andrew expected this. But the statesman still held the paper loosely in his hand.

It was a temptation.

Andrew bounded forward as if to open the cab door, pounced upon the paper and disappeared with it up an alley. After five minutes' dread lest he might be pursued, he struck a match and read:

"Great Titchfield Street — Branscombe 15, Churchill 11, Langtry 8, Gladstone 4.

" Mortimer Street — Langtry 11, Branscombe 9, Gladstone 6, Mary Anderson 6, Churchill 3.

"Margaret Street — Churchill 7, Anderson 6, Branscombe 5, Gladstone 4, Chamberlain 4.

" Smaller streets — Churchill 14, Branscombe

13, Gladstone 9, Langtry 9. Totals for to-day: Churchill 35, Langtry 28, Gladstone 23, Branscombe 42, Anderson 12, Chamberlain nowhere." Then followed, as if in a burst of passion, " Branscombe still leading — confound her."

Andrew saw that Lord Randolph had been calculating fame from vesta boxes.

For a moment this discovery sent Andrew's mind wandering. Miss Branscombe's photographs obstructed the traffic. Should not this be put a stop to? Ah, but she was a woman!

This recalled him to himself. Lord Randolph had departed, probably for St. Stephen's.

Andrew jumped into a hansom. He felt like an exotic in a glass frame.

"The House," he said.

What a pity his mother could not have seen him then!

Perhaps Andrew was prejudiced. Undoubtedly he was in a mood to be easily pleased.

In his opinion at any rate, Lord Randolph's speech that night on the Irish question was the best he ever delivered.

It came on late in the evening, and he stuck to his text like a clergyman. He quoted from Hansard to prove that Mr. Gladstone did not know what he was talking about; he blazed out against the Parnellites till they were called to order. The ironical members who cried " Hear, hear," regretted it.

He had never been wittier, never more convincing, never so magnificently vituperative.

Andrew was lifted out of himself. He jumped in ecstasy to his feet. It was he who led the applause.

He felt that this was a worthy close to a brilliant career.

We oldsters looking on more coolly could have seen where the speech was lacking, so far as Andrew was concerned. It is well known that when a great man, of whom there will be biographers, is to die a violent death, his last utterances are strangely significant, as if he foresaw his end.

There was nothing of this in Lord Randolph's speech.

The House was thinning when the noble lord rose to go. Andrew joined him at the gate.

The Scotchman's nervous elation had all gone. A momentary thrill passed through his veins as he remembered that in all probability they would never be together again. After that he was quite calm.

The night was black.

The rain had ceased, but for an occasional drop shaken out of a shivering star.

But for a few cabs rolling off with politicians, Whitehall was deserted.

The very tax-collectors seemed to have got to bed.

Lord Randolph shook hands with two or three other members homeward bound, walked a short

distance with one of them, and then set off towards
his hotel alone.

His pace was leisurely, as that of a man in pro-
found thought.

There was no time to be lost; but Andrew
dallied.

Once he crept up and could have done it. He
thought he would give him another minute.

There was a footstep behind, and he fell back.

It was Sir William Harcourt. Lord Randolph
heard him, and, seeing who it was, increased his
pace.

The illustrious Liberal slackened at the same
moment.

Andrew bit his lip and hurried on.

Some time was lost in getting round Sir William.

He was advancing in strides now.

Lord Randolph saw that he was pursued.

When Andrew began to run, he ran too.

There were not ten yards between them at
Whitehall Place.

A large man turning the corner of Great Scotland Yard fell against Andrew. He was wheeled
aside, but Mr. Chaplin had saved a colleague's life.

With a cry Andrew bounded on, his knife glis-
tening.

Trafalgar Square was a black mass.

Lord Randolph took Northumberland Avenue
in four steps, Andrew almost on the top of him.

BETTER DEAD

As he burst through the door of the Grand Hotel, his pursuer made one tremendous leap, and his knife catching Lord Randolph in the heel, carried away his shoe.

Andrew's face had struck the steps.

He heard the word " Fenian."

There was a rushing to and fro of lights.

Springing to his feet, he thrust the shoe into his pocket and went home.

CHAPTER IX

" Tie this muffler round your neck."

It was the president who spoke. Andrew held his thesis in his hand.

" But the rooms are so close," he said.

" That has nothing to do with it," said the president. The blood rushed to his head, and then left him pale.

" But why ? " asked Andrew.

" For God's sake, do as I bid you," said his companion, pulling himself by a great effort to the other side of the room.

" You have done it ? " he asked, carefully avoiding Andrew's face.

" Yes, but — "

" Then we can go in to the others. Remember what I told you about omitting the first seven pages. The society won't stand introductory remarks in a thesis."

The committee were assembled in the next room.

When the young Scotchman entered with the president, they looked him full in the neck.

" He is suffering from cold," the president said.

No one replied, but angry eyes were turned on the speaker. He somewhat nervously placed his young friend in a bad light, with a table between him and his hearers.

Then Andrew began.

" The Society for Doing Without," he read, " has been tried and found wanting. It has now been in existence for some years, and its members have worked zealously, though unostentatiously.

" I am far from saying a word against them. They are patriots as true as ever petitioned against the Channel Tunnel."

" No compliments," whispered the president, warningly. Andrew hastily turned a page, and continued:

" But what have they done ? Removed an individual here and there. That is the extent of it.

" You have been pursuing a half-hearted policy. You might go on for centuries at this rate before you made any perceptible difference in the streets.

" Have you ever seen a farmer thinning turnips ? Gentlemen, there is an example for you. My proposal is that everybody should have to die on reaching the age of forty-five years.

" It has been the wish of this society to avoid the prejudices engendered of party strife. But though you are a social rather than a political organisation, you cannot escape politics. You do not call yourselves Radicals, but you work for Radicalism. What is Radicalism? It is a desire to get a chance. This is an aspiration inherent in the human breast. It is felt most keenly by the poor.

" Make the poor rich, and the hovels, the misery, the immorality, and the crime of the East End disappear. It is infamous, say the Socialists, that this is not done at once. Yes, but how is it to be done? Not, as they hold, by making the classes and the masses change places. Not on the lines on which the society has hitherto worked. There is only one way, and I make it my text to-night. Fortunately, it presents no considerable difficulties.

" It is well known in medicine that the simplest — in other words, the most natural — remedies may be the most efficacious.

" So it is in the social life. What shall we do, Society asks, with our boys? I reply, Kill off the parents.

" There can be little doubt that forty-five years is long enough for a man to live. Parents must see that. Youth is the time to have your fling.

" Let us see how this plan would revolutionise the world. It would make statesmen hurry up. At present, they are nearly fifty before you hear of them. How can we expect the country to be properly governed by men in their dotage?

" Again, take the world of letters. Why does the literary aspirant have such a struggle? Simply because the profession is over-stocked with seniors. I would like to know what Tennyson's age is, and Ruskin's, and Browning's. Every one of them is over seventy, and all writing away yet as lively as you like. It is a crying scandal.

" Things are the same in medicine, art, divinity, law — in short, in every profession and in every trade.

" Young ladies cry out that this is not a marrying age. How can it be a marrying age, with grey-headed parents everywhere ? Give young men their chance, and they will marry younger than ever, if only to see their children grown up before they die.

" A word in conclusion. Looking around me, I cannot but see that most, if not all, of my hearers have passed what should plainly be the allotted span of life to man. You would have to go.

" But, gentlemen, you would do so feeling that you were setting a noble example. Younger, and — may I say ? — more energetic men would fill your places and carry on your work. You would hardly be missed."

Andrew rolled up his thesis blandly, and strode into the next room to await the committee's decision. It cannot be said that he felt the slightest uneasiness.

The president followed, shutting the door behind him.

"You have just two minutes," he said.

Andrew could not understand it.

His hat was crushed on to his head, his coat flung at him; he was pushed out at a window, squeezed through a grating and tumbled into a passage.

"What is the matter?" he asked, as the president dragged him down a back street.

The president pointed to the window they had just left.

Half a dozen infuriated men were climbing from it in pursuit. Their faces, drunk with rage, awoke Andrew to a sense of his danger.

"They were drawing lots for you when I left the room," said the president.

"But what have I done?" gasped Andrew.

"They didn't like your thesis. At least, they make that their excuse."

"Excuse?"

"Yes; it was really your neck that did it."

By this time they were in a cab, rattling into Gray's Inn Road.

"They are a poor lot," said Andrew fiercely, "if they couldn't keep their heads over my neck."

"They are only human," retorted the president. "For Heaven's sake, pull up the collar of your coat."

His fingers were itching, but Andrew did not notice it.

" Where are we going ? " he asked.

" To King's Cross. The midnight express leaves in twenty minutes. It is your last chance."

Andrew was in a daze. When the president had taken his ticket for Glasgow he was still groping.

The railway officials probably thought him on his honeymoon.

They sauntered along the platform beyond the lights.

Andrew, who was very hot, unloosened his greatcoat.

In a moment a great change came over his companion. All the humanity went from his face, his whole figure shook, and it was only by a tremendous effort that he chained his hands to his side.

" Your neck," he cried; " cover it up."

Andrew did not understand. He looked about him for the committee.

" There are none of them here," he said feebly.

The president had tried to warn him.

Now he gave way.

The devil that was in him leapt at Andrew's throat.

The young Scotchman was knocked into a goods waggon, with the president twisted round him.

At that moment there was heard the whistle of the Scotch express.

"Your blood be on your own head," cried the president, yielding completely to temptation.

His fingers met round the young man's neck.

"My God!" he murmured, in a delirious ecstasy, "what a neck, what a neck!"

Just then his foot slipped.

He fell. Andrew jumped up and kicked him as hard as he could three times.

Then he leapt to the platform, and, flinging himself into the moving train, fell exhausted on the seat.

Andrew never thought so much of the president again. You cannot respect a man and kick him.

CHAPTER X

The first thing Andrew did on reaching Wheens was to write to his London landlady to send on his box with clothes by goods train; also his tobacco pouch, which he had left on the mantel-piece, and two pencils which she would find in the tea-caddy.

Then he went around to the manse.

The minister had great news for him.

The master of the Wheens Grammar School had died. Andrew had only to send in his testimonials, and the post was his.

The salary was £200 per annum, with an assistant and the privilege of calling himself rector.

This settled, Andrew asked for Clarrie. He was humbler now than he had been, and in our disappointments we turn to woman for solace.

Clarrie had been working socks for him, and would have had them finished by this time had she known how to turn the heel.

It is his sweetheart a man should be particular about. Once he settles down it does not much matter whom he marries.

All this and much more the good old minister pointed out to Andrew. Then he left Clarrie and her lover together.

The winsome girl held one of the socks on her knee — who will chide her ? — and a tear glistened in her eye.

Andrew was a good deal affected.

"Clarrie," he said softly, " will you be my wife ? "

She clung to him in reply. He kissed her fondly.

"Clarrie, beloved," he said nervously, after a long pause, " how much are seven and thirteen?"

"Twenty-three," said Clarrie, putting up her mouth to his.

Andrew laughed a sad vacant laugh.

He felt that he would never understand a woman. But his fingers wandered through her tobacco-coloured hair.

He had a strange notion.

"Put your arms round my neck," he whispered.

Thus the old, old story was told once more.

A month afterwards the president of the Society for Doing Without received by post a box of bride-cake, adorned with the silver gilt which is also largely used for coffins.

.   .   .   .   .

MORE than two years have passed since Andrew's marriage, and already the minister has two sweet grandchildren, in whom he renews his youth.

Except during school-hours their parents' married life is one long honeymoon.

Clarrie has put Lord Randolph Churchill's shoe into a glass case on the piano, and, as is only natural, Andrew is now a staunch Conservative.

Domesticated and repentant, he has renounced the devil and all her works.

Sometimes, when thinking of the past, the babble of his lovely babies jars upon him, and, still half-dreaming, he brings their heads close together.

At such a time all the anxious mother has to say is:

" Andrew ! "

Then with a start he lays them gently in a heap on the floor, and, striding the room, soon regains his composure.

For Andrew has told Clarrie all the indiscretions of his life in London, and she has forgiven everything.

Ah, what will not a wife forgive !